# MEET MATILDA
# ROCKET BUILDER

## WRITTEN BY DOM CONLON
## ILLUSTRATED BY HEIDI CANNON

uclanpublishing

# Chapter 1

## HELLO AND GOODBYE

Hi. This is the scientific journal of Matilda Musk, written for all humankind in case I don't make it back.

It contains all the research of my journey to the Moon.

This is the Moon!

I know, right? We've only just met and here I am saying that I'm outta here.

The Eagle (Apollo 11) landed here!

And not just outta here, but WAY, WAY outta here.

The reason I'm doing this is because everywhere I look people on Earth are complaining. They're complaining about the weather, about the news, about school (OK, that last one might just be my brother). They've stopped seeing what great things people are doing and this has begun to get on my nerves.

By landing on the Moon I can show everyone in the world that things aren't so bad; that we can do brilliant things.

Like when Mrs Hulme saw how Kareem Amin was upset when he struggled with his poetry

she told him to talk about science.
Kareem loves science as much as
I do and so he talked about how
all the bits which make us — all
the atoms — are first made in
the heart of a star. As he spoke,
Kareem cheered right up and,
because he talked about it so
beautifully, everyone else felt
great too.

Kareem

Mrs Hulme showed Kareem
what he could do and said this
was like poetry too.

That's a small example, and it was enough
for us, but if I'm going to make the whole
world look up then I need to do something

**MUCH BIGGER.**

Now, you don't know me, and I don't even know you, but I do know what you're thinking. You're thinking I'm as daft as a snowman in summer because how can I, a ten-year-old kid, go to the Moon? Do I have wings? Do I have jet-powered boots and a magic space helmet? Do I have a billionaire aunt with a spaceship in her underground lair?

Nope. I don't have any of those things. **BUT** I have something better — **BRAINS.** And I'm determined to use them to make the world look up.

See, everyone smiles a **LOT** more when things like the World Cup or the Olympics are on. It's as though we all really want to be happy but feel like we need an excuse first. Which is daft, if you think about it. We need excuses to get out of the bad things in life, like detention

4

or visiting cousins, but we don't need them to do great things.

Seeing how Mrs Hulme encouraged Kareem has encouraged me too.

SO HERE'S WHAT I THINK: I think the problem is that we don't encourage each other often enough. There are too many arguments, too much name-calling and too much telling each other that things suck. We're just not used to saying "you can do this" any more.

My annoying little brother

That's why I wish we'd do more amazing things.

Like going to the Moon — that was amazing.

On **May 26th, 1961**, the president of the United States of America, John F Kennedy, said "you can do this". Sort of. What he actually said was:

**"I do say that space can be explored and mastered without feeding the fires of war."**

Things were about to get exciting. The world was listening.

He went on to say:

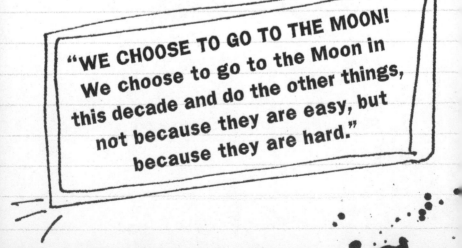

**"WE CHOOSE TO GO TO THE MOON! We choose to go to the Moon in this decade and do the other things, not because they are easy, but because they are hard."**

In saying this he challenged the people in his country to do an extraordinary thing: to send three people into space and put two of them on the Moon.

Wow. Right? WOW.

And they did it too. On **July 20th, 1969**, Neil Armstrong and Buzz Aldrin landed on the Moon whilst Michael Collins stayed in orbit around it.

More than fifty years have passed since those four boots kicked up the lunar dust. Fifty years since Neil Armstrong said:

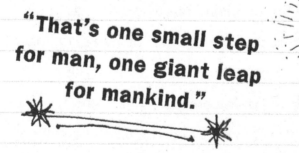

**"That's one small step for man, one giant leap for mankind."**

In that time, LOADS of other things have happened. Televisions became more popular in colour. Then they became flat. And then they could fit into our lovely pockets. Computers were once the size of a house. Then there was one in every house, and then ... yes, you guessed it ... they could fit into our pockets. We got personal stereos, we got mobile phones (which fit into pockets) and we got the Internet.

## WE DID ALL THIS IN HALF A CENTURY.

So I reckon that the older technology gets, the easier it becomes to make. Or at least it does sometimes. I can build my own telephone and my own computer if I want to. I've looked on the Internet and the parts can all be bought and there are plenty of instructions on how to assemble them. I could even build a car!

So if we can do all those things, then how hard can it be to build an old spaceship and send it to the Moon? That technology is now over fifty years old which is, like, even older than my dad, and we've made miles better stuff since then. I may be just a kid, but kids do amazing things all the time. So this kid is going to find out how to build a spaceship.

And then she's going to build it.

I've said this before but I'm going to say it again, so listen up: I've got brains. I'm not bragging but I'm not ashamed of saying it either.

And because I've got brains I can see that none of this will be easy. After all, NASA had **400,000** people. I've got me. But, in my defence, NASA had to invent the tech. I just need to follow the instructions and get an adult to use the welding torch.

I mean, really. How difficult can it be?

## Chapter 2

# MEASURING UP

I told Kareem my plan. I think he's the only person in the world who would understand and not go telling on me. I mean, my dad would understand but he'd also tell me to put a coat on because it's cold in space.

Kareem is just as curious as me and thinks anything is possible. I said if we had a time machine we could just go back and sneak onboard one of the Apollo spaceships but he

said that's cheating. He suggested I make a list
and break the problem down.

So get ready to learn, fellow space explorer,
because here comes . . .

MAJOR MATILDA'S LUNAR LIST:

1. Leave Earth
2. Fly to the Moon
3. Land on the Moon
4. Return to Earth

Leaving Earth sounds easy — I do that each
time I jump. To tick off item number 1 and leave
Earth, I just need to jump a bit higher. That's
going to take a lot of leg power. If I wanted to
jump to the Moon then I'd need to jump quite

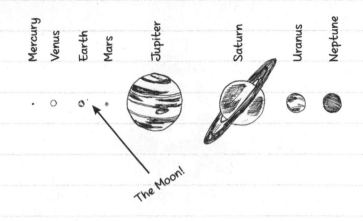

Mercury  Venus  Earth  Mars  Jupiter  Saturn  Uranus  Neptune

The Moon!

a bit higher. The Moon is **384,400 km** away (depending on where it is on its orbit around Earth). That's further than I've ever been. I once went to France and that took almost a day by train and boat and I slept most of the way. But I was a lot younger then and this time I'm not going by train or boat, I'm going to fly to the Moon in my homemade spaceship.

Straightforward isn't the same as simple. The key to this entire project, this entire properly brilliant, awe-inspiring, first ten-year-old-in-space project, is information.

Knowledge is power, as Mrs Hulme likes to say. That's why I'm going to learn as much as I can about what I'm doing. I'm leaving no stone unturned, no book unopened, no mad scientist idea unexplored.

## THINGS I ALREADY KNOW INCLUDE:

There's no air in space. This is known as a 'vacuum' which means it's empty. If I open the door of my spaceship up there then all my air will rush out and I won't be able to breathe. **GAME OVER.**

There's very little gravity in space. Gravity is the force which keeps us on the ground. Everything pulls everything towards it. The bigger the object, the stronger the effect of gravity. So the further away from Earth I go, the less its gravity will affect me. That means I'll be floating around in my spaceship.

And ... I think that's all I really know at the moment. Yikes! I've got a lot to learn. Kareem will help though.

Let's go to item number two: FLY TO THE MOON. I just remembered something else! I knew that the gap between Earth and the Moon is big but it turns out it's bigger than I thought. In photos, it often looks as though the Moon is circling (more accurately, the Moon's orbit is an ellipse so it should really be called 'ellipticalling,' but that's not a word) close to Earth. Little did I know that **384,400 km** is a big enough space to fit EVERY OTHER PLANET (Mercury, Venus, Mars, Jupiter, Saturn, Uranus and Neptune) in.

TRUE FACT!

To put that another way, if Mum drove me to the Moon and stuck to the UK speed limit of

70 mph (which is the same as saying 113 kph),
then it would take us 142 days to get there.

And that's without a toilet break.

Are we there yet?

No!

Are we there yet?

No!

Are we . . .

Ha ha ha! I could carry on doing that FOR
EVER. But I won't.

Item number three on my list is 'land on
the Moon'. Now, I'll be honest, every time I've
watched the film of the first landing I've had
this thought: it doesn't look too far to the
surface. But actually, the Command Service
Module (which was the bit they kept in orbit)
was at an altitude of **110 km** before it let go
of the Lunar Module. That means I'll need to
guide it down.

That might be tricky, but not impossible —
even for a ten-year-old (hey, we're all highly
trained video game experts here). But hang on a
minute . . . Neil Armstrong almost crashed when
he was landing, so I'm going to leave number
three on my list as a maybe.

Finally, item number four, or, as I like to call
it, my

**Triumphant Return
to Earth.**

I got lost on a tour of the high school I'll be going to, so I'm not confident on this one. At first, I was thinking "it's big and blue, how can I miss?" but everything I've been reading about how the Apollo 13 crew had a real will-they-won't-they point of almost missing our enormous planet has made me rethink this. Mental note: look into space navigation. How did the astronauts find their way? Is there a Google Maps for the Solar System? At the next asteroid, turn left. I don't think there is but I'm going to need something.

After all, space is a pretty big place. Which also means . . . I'm going to get hungry.

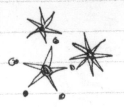

# Chapter 3

## FOOD FOR THOUGHT

Mrs Hulme says my stomach must be a gateway to another universe because I'm, like, never not hungry. We had exams yesterday. That meant sitting for an entire hour without eating. An entire hour. Oh, and answering some questions too. But . . . food! Mum ordered pizza as a treat and that got me thinking about how much food I'll need to take with me when I go to the Moon.

To help me figure this out, I emptied the fridge. And the freezer. And the cupboards.

Like I said:

# I GET HUNGRY.

It's a long way to the Moon, though.

In **1969**, it took Michael Collins, Buzz Aldrin and Neil Armstrong four days to cross that distance. They set off on **July 16th** and landed on **July 20th**. Actually, it took a bit less. It took them about four days, because they didn't land the moment they arrived.

| Sun | Mon | Tues | Weds | Thurs | Fri | Sat |
|---|---|---|---|---|---|---|
| **13** | **14** | **15** | **16** | **17** | **18** | **19** |
| | | | Launch | | | |

| Sun | Mon | Tues | Weds | Thurs | Fri | Sat |
|---|---|---|---|---|---|---|
| **20** | **21** | **22** | **23** | **24** | **25** | **26** |
| Land on Moon | | Flush toilet | Change socks | Tea at Mum's | | |

They had a look at the surface from orbit, ate a bit, slept a bit, separated the Lunar Module from the Command Module (more of that later) and generally faffed about the way I do when Dad asks me to get ready quickly. But going to the Moon? There's no WAY I'd spend an entire day looking at the Moon before going down there.

**384,400 km** is a long way though. A really long way. The more I think about item two, the more this looks a bit trickier than just walking to the park.

But here's a thought: could they have done it quicker? Not that I'm impatient (OK, I am — another time I got lost was when I was seven years old and got fed up waiting for my dad to pick me up from school. I managed to get as far as the sweet shop before I was found. Luckily I had some pocket money and bought a packet of Millions and three jelly snakes).

Lunar 1, the tiny craft first sent to photograph the Moon, took just thirty-six hours to get there. But that wasn't trying to get into orbit, and orbits (as I'll see) are way trickier. Four days is a reasonable aim.

If I'm going to spend such a long time in space, zipping across the void like some kind of video game character, I'll need three things: food, fuel and air. Because if I don't, then I'm in more trouble than a fish in a desert. And life isn't a video game. I don't get to press 'start' again.

Four days to get there, two days to get back. Let's have another two days to enjoy a good look around. That makes my journey time an epic eight days. If I stick to three meals a day then I'll need **twenty-four packed lunches** (because I multiply three by eight). Oh, but I'd better not go alone. The original Apollo missions had three people on board. That's a sensible number, for reasons I'll go into later. So, according to my calculations that comes to seventy-two parcels of food (multiply the twenty-four lunches by three people). Plus snacks. Let's not forget snacks. What shall I take?

Pizza and Oreos? Seventy-two bags of Haribo? Crumpets? Tubs of ice cream and some cans of Dandelion and Burdock? Everything I took out of the fridge, the freezer and the cupboards?

Yum!

Dad asked me where I was going with all that food so I told him that I was just trying to figure out how much I'd need to take on a camping trip.

"How are you going to carry it?" he said.

Which totally made me think.

I mean, I know I don't have to carry it all in a rucksack, but one thing I do know already is that most of a spaceship is fuel. When it comes to space travel, **WEIGHT** is everything. The more weight you carry, the more fuel it takes to lift it.

I worked out how much weight I'd be taking if I only took pizza.

A pizza can weigh around **900 grams** — and probably more because I like my extra toppings. If I add another hundred grams for the box then we have one kilogram for just one pizza. For seventy-two pizzas that would add **seventy-two kilograms** to what we are trying to take into space. That's like taking two friends with me — fine if I need extra hands to do the washing up but not so good when I come to figure out how much fuel I need.

Luckily, NASA had a plan and it's a plan I can happily tuck into.

# SPACE FOOD!

I went to the Science Museum and bought a pack of ice-cream space food from the gift shop. It was rock hard, but once the spit in my mouth softened it then it tasted really good. That sounds way grosser than it was and I promise not to spit on anyone else's food.

The best thing about using proper space food is that I'll save a lot of weight and storage space because it's light and packs away really neatly. I have a feeling that this is going to be important.

In **1969,** space food was a bit different to what we can buy today. Opening the packets involved using scissors, and things could — and did — go wrong. I'm not trying to do everything the way they did for the sake of it — I just want to get there using tried and tested methods. If I can use something better then I'm totally OK with that.

Knowing all this means food isn't going to be so much of a problem.

You remember how I said Kareem had a problem with poetry? Well, it was my turn yesterday and I recited the

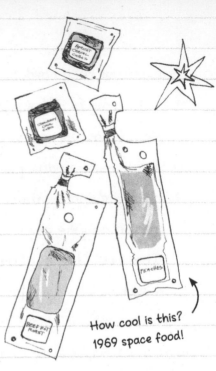

How cool is this? 1969 space food!

poem I'd learnt only I did it really fast because I wanted to finish so I could go out and talk to my friends about space food because I think it's really amazing how food can be dry and yet . . . anyway, that bit doesn't matter because what matters is that I was talking so fast that Miss said <u>"WHOA, MATILDA. SLOW DOWN AND TAKE A BREATH"</u> and I had a brainwave right there and then.

Breathing is important.

And there's no air in space.

So if I'm going to be able

to breathe, then I'll have to

take air with me. How do I do that? Do I fill

balloons?

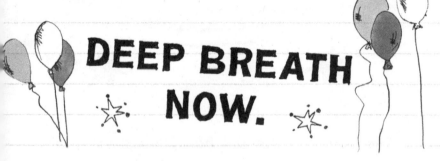

# DEEP BREATH
# NOW.

This is where it starts getting complicated.

# Chapter 4

## TAKE A BREATH

The more I read about how NASA sent people to the Moon, the more I find I don't know stuff. Like, I thought breathing air was the same as breathing oxygen, but it isn't. It's made of oxygen, nitrogen, carbon dioxide, argon and methane.

SO HERE'S A QUESTION: what's it mostly made of? What's the biggest part?

Do you think it's mostly oxygen?

Do you think it's mostly nitrogen?

Or do you think it's mostly carbon dioxide?

If you think the answer is oxygen or carbon dioxide then

hold your breath and count to 8,000.

If you think the answer is nitrogen then you may let out a sigh of relief because it is.

Everyone has heard of oxygen (I went into hospital last year and had to wear an oxygen mask), so it's understandable that you'd think of the air as mostly oxygen but it actually only makes up something like **21%** of the air we breathe. A whopping **78%** is nitrogen. The final **1%** is the other stuff.

I'm going to need to breathe in space and,

as you probably already know, there is no air in space. Mum says I've enough hot air in me to send a balloon to the Moon, but I know she's joking so I'll need to take some extra. LOTS EXTRA.

Now, here's something I didn't know: when I'm in space I won't be breathing the same sort of air we breathe here on Earth.

You see, out in space, people can safely breathe pure oxygen.

During the Apollo programme (and earlier in the Gemini programme), astronauts breathed oxygen in space for weeks at a time. They were just fine, thanks for asking. On Earth, they'd have had all sorts of problems (and even more if they did it whilst deep sea diving) because our lungs aren't built to deal with pure oxygen here.

So why is there one rule for Earth and one rule for space?

I asked Kareem why this might be. He's the only other person I know who reads about science. He said it probably has something to do with a force called air pressure  but then asked me to leave him alone because he was busy with something else.

I don't know what could be more important than helping me go to space but . . . whatever.

**I CAN DO THIS.**

The force Kareem mentioned is more accurately called atmospheric pressure. It means the weight of stuff pressing in around us. It can be air or it can be something else, because the atmosphere isn't always made up of air (like under the sea, for example).

Here's how it works.

If I blow a tiny bit of air into a balloon, the rubber remains floppy and wrinkled. The more air I blow into it, the more the balloon stretches. That's because the air pressure inside is increasing as the rubber walls tighten around it. But there is also pressure put on the balloon from the outside too. The outside air squeezes the balloon and the balloon squeezes the air inside it.

The pressure on Earth, at sea level, is about **fifteen pounds per square inch**. If you dive into the sea, the atmospheric pressure will increase. If you climb a mountain then the pressure will decrease because the air is thinner — there's less of it.

Breathing pure oxygen is fine if the pressure is low enough, like at the **five pounds per square inch used** for most (but not all) of the Apollo missions.

That sounds simple, but it isn't. In fact there are some really serious dangers here.

During a ground-based test of Apollo 1 in 1966, three astronauts (Ed White, Gus Grissom and Roger Chaffee) climbed into the Command Module. That's the bit of the spaceship right near the top, shaped like a cone. And once they were inside, the regular air you and I breathe was changed for pure oxygen.

Unfortunately, two things went wrong: firstly the pressure of the air was too high. NASA technicians had set it to roughly what we have here on Earth at sea level. The second thing which went wrong was a fire started.

Unless you want to toast marshmallows or are trying to be rescued from a desert island, fires are dangerous. Add pure oxygen to this and it's even more dangerous.

For Apollo 1 it was DISASTROUS.

If the air pressure had been at the lower level (**five pounds per square inch**) then the fire might have been a lot easier to contain because fire doesn't spread so quickly in that sort of environment.

Imagine lots of people crowded together in a room. You could pass something from one person to the next really quickly because they are close. If there were only two or three people in the room then they'd have to travel further to pass something.

That's kind of what happened with the fire. It jumped from one oxygen molecule to another really quickly because the molecules were packed together in the spaceship.

Sadly, the fire quickly burnt through the entire craft and killed all three astronauts.

So why would I want to breathe pure oxygen in space when I don't do that here on Earth? The answer, once again, comes down to weight. Oxygen is a lot lighter than the air we breathe. And lighter air means it doesn't take as much fuel to lift it into space. If the Apollo missions had used a regular, Earth-like mix, then it would have been heavier because even air weighs something. Add to this the fact that the equipment needed to store and deliver it to the astronauts is more complicated and (can you guess?) HEAVIER.

Even with the simpler, pure oxygen solution, I'm going to have to take a lot of spare air.

On Earth, the average person breathes around one hundred litres of air every hour. But remember when we talked about oxygen making up **21%** of the air? That's all I need to take with me! Three cheers for space-saving measures!

This means of the **one hundred litres per hour** I'd breathe if I were on Earth, I will only be breathing **twenty litres of oxygen** when I'm in space. Even so, that still adds up to **480 litres** every day. That's for each person. **480** multiplied by **3** equals **1,440**. Multiply that by **8** (for the number of days) and I need to take with me a chest-inflating **11,520 litres of oxygen**.

# SO MUCH MATHS! SO MUCH STUFF!

And that's not including the oxygen I need to help fuel the rocket.

Now things are going to start getting really heavy. But first I need to find out what happens when I breathe out.

# Chapter 5

## WASTE NOT WANTED

Kareem still isn't talking to me as much as he used to so I've been to the library a LOT this week. I think I sort of took breathing for granted and I needed to find out more. Besides, a certain SOMEONE, WHO SHALL REMAIN NAMELESS (Noah B), had a really smelly lunch and breathed ALL OVER ME and it was gross but it made me think.

I need to take oxygen along with me if

I want to keep breathing. Which I totally do, of course. Oxygen will keep my spaceship simple and light in a way that trying to adapt it for regular air won't. This isn't, however, the whole story because just as what goes up must come down (when under the influence of gravity), then what goes in must come out.

We breathe in. We breathe out.

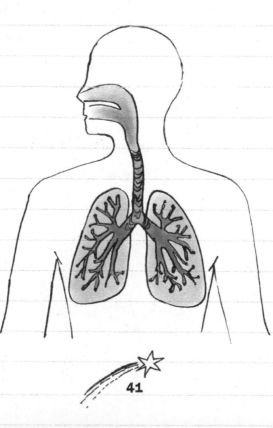

Our lungs take what they need and get rid of the rest. The process of taking the good stuff produces a waste gas called carbon dioxide.

Carbon dioxide is not something we can breathe back in again. It gets absorbed into the blood, making it acidic. If there's too much carbon dioxide in our blood, it becomes poisonous. That's why anywhere people have to breathe oxygen (like in a hospital or in a spaceship) they will need something which can remove the carbon dioxide.

On Earth, green plants and trees do a lot of this work for us, but I can't take a tree with

me into space, so I'll need something called a scrubber which will clean the breathed-out air.

OK! It's **HISTORY TIME AGAIN!**

A billion years ago, in 1970, and after two successful moon landings, it was the turn of astronauts, Jim Lovell, Jack Swigert and Fred Haise to launch into space as part of the Apollo 13 mission.

It was the mission in which things

# EXPLODED,

power supplies ran low and a vital part of the spaceship failed.

**Spoiler alert:** everyone got back safely, but that was because of some really smart thinking to fix the air scrubbers.

When they were in space, an oxygen tank exploded and ruined the part of the spaceship called the Service Module. This meant that the astronauts couldn't land on the Moon. They had to whizz around it and head back to Earth.

Unfortunately, things weren't quite as simple as just sitting out the journey time playing I-Spy.

The problem had also caused a shortage in the carbon dioxide scrubbers. The astronauts had enough air to last the journey but because they were breathing out, they needed the air to be kept clean.

Luckily, the clever folk back at NASA figured out a way to convert some of the scrubbers from a different part of the spaceship so that they would work with the bit they were in and everyone breathed easy.

# PHEW!

Building my own carbon dioxide scrubbers isn't difficult. In fact I could probably do a guest appearance on Blue Peter to show everyone how.

During the Apollo missions, the spaceships used scrubbers which contained a chemical called lithium hydroxide. There's no way I can buy some of that but I can use algae, or I could buy some ready made.

We exhale out roughly 1.5 kilograms of carbon dioxide every day. I'll be taking two of my best friends who talk as much as I do, so there's no way we can limit the amount of carbon dioxide by keeping quiet and not breathing out so much. Even so, over the **eight-day journey**, we will breathe out:

**1.5 kilograms of carbon dioxide**

multiplied by

**3 people**

multiplied by

**8 days.**

That comes to a hefty **thirty-six kilograms of carbon dioxide**. And curiously, that number is also about half the number of meals we will need.

I can make my own scrubber using an aquarium pump, a tube and an old lemonade bottle filled with water and algae. According to the instructions I've read, I'll need three of these. Perhaps I should take five or six, just in case. This is where decisions become tricky. Every extra thing I take along with me adds weight to my spaceship.

And whilst I'm writing about waste . . .
there's something else I'll need to get rid of. My
poo and my wee.

The wee bit is quite simple and, as Apollo 9
astronaut Russell Schweickart said, is:

**"The most beautiful sight in orbit."**

All the toilet stuff on the Apollo spaceship
was designed for men. Despite training and
passing all the requirements, not a single woman
was chosen for the Apollo missions. In fact, it
took until **1983** for **Sally Ride** to become the
first American female in space. The Russians, on
the other hand, sent **Valentina Tereshkova**
into space in **1961**.

So when it comes to the toilet, I'm going to
need a clean sheet of paper (or at least a new
chapter).

# Chapter 6

# HOW TO PEE IN ZERO G

This is a bit embarrassing to tell you, but I've got to be honest because getting to the Moon means looking at absolutely everything. That includes how many times I go to the toilet.

I usually have one poo a day. Some people have fewer, some more. The poo might weigh around **300 grams** (I didn't weigh it — I got into enough trouble emptying the cupboards so I wasn't about to take the kitchen scales into the bathroom).

**Here's a weird fact though:** we lose a little bit of weight when we poo, but not 300 grams.

So I'll be in space for eight days. That means I'll have eight poos. There are going to be three of us (I still haven't decided who yet because Kareem isn't talking to me). So eight poos multiplied by three people equals twenty-four.

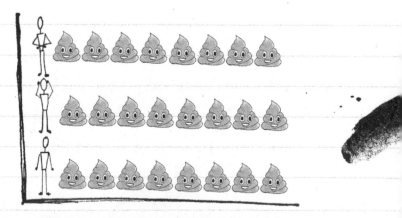

That means we will produce just over **seven kilograms** of waste. That isn't too bad. It's like seven bags of sugar. But who wants to keep that in the spaceship? I'm going to have to find a way to blast it all into space and hope it's not the first human thing to make alien contact.

That would be awkward. "Take me to your leader! Hello? Hello?"

Now, to talk about this more I need to remind myself that a vacuum is a space with nothing in it and that everything will get sucked out into it if I open a door into a vacuum. And the second thing I need to remind myself of is that gravity is the force of attraction — what keeps us on the ground rather than floating around like human balloons.

With that in mind, did you know that if wee is sucked out into the vacuum of space it will instantly freeze, turning into tiny ice crystals which then scatter into the void? Space is big and it is very very cold.

Wheeeeeeeeeeeeeeeeee!

Having a wee has never sounded so beautiful.

The (male) astronauts of the Apollo missions could wee into a hose (called the urine transfer system) which was attached to a bag (called the urine collection and transfer assembly) which then fed through into a system which

shot the liquid into space. This involved a special valve between the hose and the outside of the spaceship. That last bit was called the urine receptacle assembly and meant that one twist would let the vacuum of space suck all the liquid out. That's just like a vacuum cleaner. Just don't try to use one on the toilet. Trust me on this.

The last part had a honeycomb panel on it which was made up of lots of thin tubes. In the low gravity, this would keep hold of the liquid. Or rather, it would do so for most of the time.

The effects of a vacuum are different to the effects of gravity. The way to think about a vacuum is to think of when Miss opens the door at the end of the day and we all run out into the playground.

The way to think about gravity is the way the more sweets someone has, the more of us will be pulled towards them.

Understanding gravity is really, really important so I'm going to learn as much as I can about it.

Hey! I have news! Kareem is still talking to me. I thought he'd fallen out with me but he said he hadn't. He was just busy trying to do something else but wouldn't tell me what. He wants to help me more and I said yes, because I'm already worrying that I won't be able to do this on my own.

I mentioned gravity to him and he became all excited.

He said the thing to remember here is that in space I'll be living in a low gravity environment (there is still some gravity, of course, otherwise the Moon would no longer orbit Earth — but we will discuss orbits and gravity later). That means, if I spill anything then it won't splash down on to the ground, it will float. That's great fun if you want to create blobs of water to play with, but less fun if the liquid is urine.

And it's even worse when we are faced with floating poo.

I don't know why he was excited about floating poo. He's weird. But **WEIRD IS GOOD**. And understanding gravity is good too.

NASA was just as interested in floating poo as Kareem is. The way they collected it all during the Apollo missions was more complicated than I will need it to be. That's because NASA was more curious about poo than I ever want to be.

54

Me, I'm in a rush to flush but NASA wanted to take a look and write a book.

I read how **Bill Anders**, one of the astronauts on **Apollo 8**, went all the way to the Moon and back (they didn't land) without having a single poo. He'd taken a special tablet to prevent him from going because doing so could be uncomfortable, inconvenient and embarrassing. More than one floating number two was reported and if things were less than solid, well...

ANYWAY... In the spirit of keeping things simple, I'm going to stick with the basics of NASA's waste management system. That involved a plastic bag, some sticky tape and plenty of hope.

I'm sorry to keep going on about this sort of thing, but it's a fact of life. And to be blunt, in space, what goes up doesn't come down.

And that's because of gravity. Or the lack of it.

I've been learning a lot about a scientist called **Isaac Newton**. I already knew a few things — like the story of him sitting beside a tree and shouting "ouch" when an apple fell on his head. For most of us this would result in apple pie, but for Isaac Newton, it led to a deep understanding of how gravity works.

He worked out that gravity is what keeps our feet on Earth. It's why stuff (depending upon its mass) falls when we let go. Our bodily functions are just as dependent upon gravity. Which is to say that in space, there's nothing telling our wee or poo to drop out. We might try to encourage the poo into the bag by pushing but it won't do the entire job. We're going to also need to help the poo come out by using our fingers. The bags used by astronauts had a special pocket called a finger cot. So you don't get dirty but you're still not going to want to pick your nose afterwards.

This reminds me of a joke: What did the constipated mathematician do? She worked the problem out with a pencil.

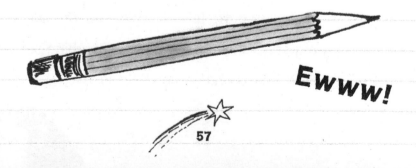

EWWW!

Maybe I'll go with the Bill Anders method.

The other thing I need to think about is what to do if I need a poo or wee when I'm walking about on the Moon. The answer, I've discovered, is simpler than even the bag.

I need a nappy.

I wish I was joking, but I'm not. Every astronaut you have ever seen walking around on the Moon wore a nappy. It was a specially designed nappy, but it was still a nappy. I can't be leaping off to find a tree to pee behind when I'm on the Moon. There are no trees. And even if there were, I still couldn't drop my trousers, could I? Not without boiling and freezing to death at the same time (but more of that later when I learn about space suits).

I'm trying not to let all this put me off building my spaceship. Gross as it is, nothing so far seems so tricky that I can't do it.

Of course, that's only because the real challenges appear once I begin to learn about the laws of physics.

# Chapter 7

## MAYBE THERE'S ANOTHER WAY

I want to start building my spaceship. I mean really building. I want to drag Mum or Dad to Tesco and see if I can add a hundred-and-eleven-metre-long steel tube to the shopping trolley (which is the height of a Saturn V spaceship). And some nachos (hey, nachos are practically space food). But I can't. I know I can't. I did find an old oil drum in the woods near my house

and wondered if I could drag it to my launch site (yes, I've chosen somewhere already) but it was pretty heavy and after I climbed into it I knew I couldn't make it work. It was too small (the Saturn V fuel stages were about ten metres in diameter).

And it smelt.

It made me think of the times my dad would change the oil in the car and I remembered a book Grandad sent me last Christmas: the Haynes manual for the Saturn V. I've got it here in front of me and it's really technical and has loads of diagrams and pictures and, well, I'm wondering whether there is another way to get to the Moon.

Like, why can't I just float to space? I love spaceships, all that juddering and smoke and BOOM. But, as I'm discovering, they are filled with very complicated machinery for very complicated reasons. So why can't I do it slowly? Why not just take my time and float up, up and away in a balloon?

In **2014**, a man called **Robert Eustace** flew in a high-tech balloon and set a world record for the longest free fall back to Earth. He managed to float up to **41,420 metres** and then jump out. It took him four minutes and twenty-seven seconds to reach the ground. This is cool. Very cool. But that isn't even halfway to the point at which space begins.

Space OFFICIALLY begins at **100,000 metres** (this is known as the **KARMAN** line), but the reason a balloon can't reach that high is down to what makes it float: helium.

Helium is a gas which is lighter than air. Which is great! I want to be lighter than air. But eventually, the atmosphere gets thinner and thinner — remember when we talked about atmospheric pressure? There's more to understand about that, but for now, let's keep it simple. At a point which is roughly **thirty-two kilometres** up, the weight of the atmosphere becomes the same as the weight of the helium and it can go no higher. I need a push to get higher.

So how about a piggy-back?

That's not such a bad idea. In **1959** an aeroplane called the **X-15** hitched a ride under a **B-52 bomber**. It was dropped (like a bomb) and then fired its rocket engines to fly even higher. Doing this meant it would need less fuel to reach high altitudes. I read that the X-15 could, and did, reach the edge of space, flown by **Joseph Walker** to a whopping **107.8 km**. But that was in **1963** and **Al Shepherd** had already been there in **1961** whilst flying **Freedom 7**. Number fans (like me) will be happy to hear he reached **187.5 km** and his flight lasted just fifteen minutes — which is basically just a playtime.

Freedom 7

Cool beans as this sounds, I have to remind myself that neither the X-15 nor Freedom 7 could reach orbit. High as they went, they were both still 'sub-orbital'.

There is a more modern spaceship which piggy-backs another plane. It's from a company called Virgin Galactic, but even that will only reach the edge of space. It isn't designed to go to the Moon.

To do that, I will need to build a bigger rocket. A much bigger rocket. The **Saturn V**, the spaceship I'm copying, stood **111 metres** tall.

Which brings me right back to one of my first points: how difficult can it be?

A rocket is what happens when:

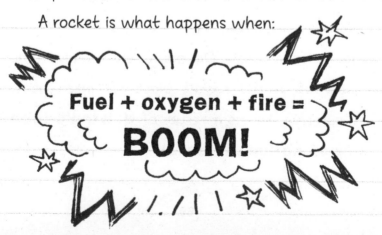

Fuel + oxygen + fire = BOOM!

Ideally that BOOM! will be controlled and not like, you know, a bomb. I'll do my best not to scatter my pocket money, or my atoms, across the launchpad.

A (controlled) explosion produces a hot gas called exhaust. The exhaust from the Saturn V rocket was a face-melting **3,000 degrees Celsius** (remember that at sea-level, water will boil in a kettle at **100 degrees Celsius**. My gran starts moaning about the weather being too hot when it's roughly **20 degrees Celsius** (then she says it's too cold when it drops below 19 degrees).

The exhaust is funnelled through a nozzle and emerges from enormous pipes where all the onlookers say 'Ooooooh' and 'Aaaaaah' as they watch the rocket blast off into space. Apparently, this is a result of **Newton's third law of motion** which says:

> **"For every action, there is an equal and opposite reaction."**

The rocket isn't pushing against the ground. The rocket is pushing against the exhaust fuel, which is pushing against the rocket.

This is a **force**. There are lots of different kinds of forces and this involves two of them: an **action force** and a **reaction force**.

I asked if I could tidy the school hall. Miss was a bit surprised that I asked (you should see my messy pencil case), but said yes.

What I wanted to do was try out an experiment.

I put on a pair of roller skates and stood on the wooden floor whilst holding a netball. It could have been any heavy object (like an elephant maybe).

Then I threw the ball. The result was that I moved in the opposite direction. The ball went forwards, I went backwards. That's because there was an **equal and opposite reaction**. I pushed the ball away from me and the ball pushed me away with the same force.

This is why I will be able to fire my rockets in space in order to move, even though there is no ground or air to push against.

Kareem walked in and saw me do this.

Actually, I rolled into him but he didn't mind. He said he'd been wanting to talk to me anyway because all this time he's been looking into how he could help me. He suggested that we build a really small rocket first and he knew how.

We built it together using a match and some tinfoil (we asked my dad if we could use the match and he watched).

We wrapped a small piece of foil tightly around the head of the match and left a tiny space where the foil touches the wood. Then we placed the rocket outside in a clear area and heated the foil using another match. AND . . .

It shot off in roughly a straight line.

Now all I need to do is scale that up to 111 metres and pack my bag!

This is going to be <u>EASY!</u>

The reaction from the rocket-firing exhaust at the ground results in thrust (the action) and lift (the reaction). And my reaction right now is to jump up and down because I feel as though I'm finally getting somewhere with this rocket building thing.

But wait, thrust and lift aren't the only forces in play.

Chapter 8

# Chapter 8

# BREAKING DOWN MY SPACESHIP

The more I learn about spaceships, the more I ask why the rocket part was so huge. The Saturn V, which the astronauts flew to the Moon during the Apollo missions, was 111 metres tall — about as long as a football field and taller than the Statue of Liberty. The bit where the astronauts sat was only twenty-seven metres tall — less if you don't include the launch escape system right at the top.

That's a lot of rocket just to send a tiny capsule into space.

A fully-fuelled Saturn V weighed 2,950,000 kilograms. The amount of stuff it needed to carry weighed just 41,000 kilograms. The proper term for 'stuff' is payload.

So why did they need all that power just to lift three people and seventy-two packed lunches into space?

To understand that, and appreciate why I can't just skip a few stages and strap fireworks to my skates, I'm going to have to understand what it takes to get into space.

To do that, I need to break down the moon rocket I want to build. Literally! I have a plastic model which splits apart and it's great for seeing which bit does what (and when).

ESCAPE
SYSTEM

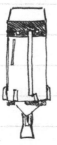

COMMAND
MODULE

LUNAR
MODULE

THIRD
STAGE
ROCKET

What I've learnt is that there are six main parts to a Saturn V.

**FIRST STAGE:** this is the lower part of the rocket and was designed to provide the energy needed to propel the rocket up to an altitude of **sixty-seven kilometres.** It had five enormous F-1 engines. Once it reached this altitude, a series of explosions cut the first stage away from the rest of the craft and sent it down into the Atlantic Ocean.

**SECOND STAGE:** once the first stage has fallen away, the five J-2 engines

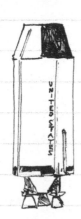

SECOND
STAGE
ROCKET

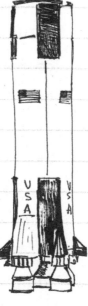

FIRST
STAGE
ROCKET

73

on the second stage of the rocket fire. A metal band called the interstage skirt is no longer needed and so gets discarded a few seconds later. Then another part, the emergency escape system, is also discarded. The Saturn V is so high up now that if anything goes wrong, the pointy part at the top of the rocket can no longer pull the command module away to safety.

And get this: so far the Saturn V has used **1,754,000 litres of fuel!** The first stage contained liquid kerosene and the second stage contained liquid hydrogen.

Which reminds me: I'm going to have to look at how to buy lots of fuel. There's probably an age limit on that though, so I'll need to get an adult involved.

**THIRD STAGE:** at a height now of **185 kilometres**, the second stage shuts down and is discarded. We are now (if you remember the **100-kilometre marker** we talked about earlier) in space. But we still have a long way to go because the third stage (with its single J-2 engine) is active for another eleven or so minutes and then the crazy thing is . . .

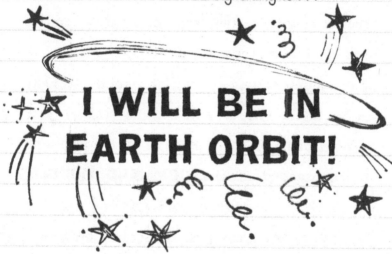

# I WILL BE IN EARTH ORBIT!

Look at me go! It's taken two full stages and a good bit of the third just to reach Earth orbit. And yet, even after all this, I still won't be high enough. High Earth orbit is where the International Space Station is (about **250 miles** or **402 kilometres**) and so to get on my way to the Moon, I will need to fire the engine once more before the third stage is also discarded.

There are three more main parts to the Saturn V that I will need:

The first is the **SERVICE MODULE**. The service module is cylindrical and has an engine used to get into (and out of) lunar orbit, as well as make any course corrections along the way. I'll be losing the service module section just before I begin re-entry into Earth's atmosphere.

The second is the **COMMAND MODULE**. That's the cone-shaped part right at the top (just below the pointy escape system bit which I'll have ditched getting into Earth orbit). The Command Module is the part I'll be sitting in when I land back on Earth.

The third part is the **LUNAR MODULE**, and that's what I need if I'm going to land on the Moon. It has two engines; one for descending (going down) and one for ascending (going up). So why does it have two engines instead of one?

The quick and easy answer is 'weight'.

In fact, the long and detailed answer is also 'weight'.

Once the Lunar Module (or LM as it's referred to) has landed, I won't need the part which helped me land. That's extra weight, so I'll leave it behind when I lift off again.

You'll have noticed that I've been getting rid of quite a lot of the Saturn V in this chapter. And on the journey home I'll be getting rid of more. That's because the more weight we have to move, the more fuel we need to move it. Getting into space is difficult enough without lugging unnecessary weight around.

It's why, in fact, I'm not building a Tintin-style rocket. In Hergé's comic, Tintin rides in

a single rocket all the way to the Moon. That means he's carrying all the fuel tanks and engines needed to get there and get back again, even after they have been emptied of fuel. The engineers at NASA did consider this for a while, because building a single rocket was simpler than building one which split into parts.

But once again, the decision came down to... you guessed it, WEIGHT!

## HOW TO SAVE WEIGHT

THINGS I NEED:

Sweets
Spacesuit
Slippers
Books
Phone
More books

THINGS I DON'T NEED:

Spare socks
Brothers
Vegetables
Toothbrush

# Chapter 9

## WEIGHT A MINUTE

It keeps on coming back to weight, doesn't it? I've had to think about the weight of food (goodbye lovely pizzas), bodily waste (goodbye and good riddance, poo), and  even the weight of the spaceship — which is why the Saturn V needed to split apart and discard bits which were no longer needed.

You see, the more something weighs, the more energy it will take to lift it. And saying the more energy it takes to lift something is like saying the more fuel you need.

But surely the more fuel I need, the heavier my spaceship will become?

And then won't I need EVEN MORE FUEL?

Will it never end? Will I have to make my spaceship bigger and bigger just to carry all the fuel it needs because it's getting bigger and bigger.

There is something called The Rocket Equation which will help me figure out how much energy is needed in order to lift the rocket into space at the right speed.

The trouble is, it's way, WAY more complicated than anything I've done at school. And I like maths.

I mean, just look at it:

$$\Delta v = v_e \ln \frac{m_0}{m_f}$$

Yeah, it made no sense to me either. It still doesn't really, but I'm sort of understanding the principle behind it because . . .

YAY FOR YOUTUBE! (Hey Mum! I'm not always wasting my time on there.)

I watched a great video on there called "The Tyranny of the Rocket Equation" by astronaut Don Pettit and it totally helped me to understand all this just as I was starting to think I may as well give up my dream of building a spaceship.

81

What I've learnt is that the rocket equation tells us how much of the rocket has to be made up of fuel in order to reach a particular location. To get to the Moon, that comes to between **83%** and **96%** of the total mass.

And the hardest part of that (and so the most fuel is needed) lies in getting into Earth's orbit.

But hang on. I've just used a word there without really explaining it: **MASS**.

What is MASS?

Mass is what we call the amount of stuff (matter) in an object. It's not the same as size.

A neutron star might be the size of a small country on Earth but contain more mass than our sun. In fact, a teaspoon of the stuff a neutron star is made from would weigh **10,000,000 tonnes**.

Try this: take a piece of aluminium foil and

gently scrunch it into the shape of a ball. You might be able to make it so that the ball is too big to fit into your fist. Now scrunch it even tighter and make it fit. The diameter of the ball has changed but the mass hasn't.

Understanding mass is important because it also affects how I'm going to understand how gravity works and why it's so difficult to reach Earth orbit.

The rocket equation uses the speed I want to go and how fast the exhaust will come out in order to figure out the amount of fuel I will need.

There are some other bits it uses too.

First I need to tell the equation where I want to go. I'm going to the Moon and to get there I have to be travelling at **fourteen kilometres per second**!

That's fast. I had to do laps around the playground and it took me about thirty minutes just to do five. There's NO WAY I will ever reach escape velocity under my own wind. And no, I don't mean my farts. Although I once . . .

Never mind that. Let's get back to building a rocket.

Knowing why I need to reach that speed involves understanding how gravity works better than I do at the moment.

Kareem said he'd help with
that because he's been trying
to learn. I asked him if he was
trying to build a spaceship too,
but he said no. I was a bit worried

Sputnik

he was going to get to the Moon before me.

So I'll talk to him about gravity soon but
for now, I'll just think about the speed and
hope the scientists got it right (**SPOILER**: they
did because it's how everything from Sputnik
to the International Space Station managed to
get into space).

When the Saturn V first launched, it
accelerated from **0 to 2.7 km/s in just 2.5
minutes**. The second stage of the rocket then
kicked in and built on that, taking it to about 7

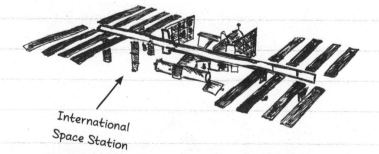

International
Space Station

km per second. Finally, the third stage took it to just under 8 km per second. That is the speed at which a craft can enter Earth orbit.

So it definitely works.

Using Saturn V as my example (because that's what I'm trying to build here), I can work out how much fuel we need. And it's a surprise.

To reach the Moon I will need **85%** of my rocket to be fuel. Using that fuel, I will have enough energy to carry **4%** as payload (that means carrying me, two friends, some food, a stack of books and a pen). The remaining **11%** is the rocket itself — the metal structure.

I know all of this because of the rocket equation. So when I get the materials to build the rocket, I can't choose granite or concrete. That would make it far too heavy and I'd need an even more mind-blowing amount of fuel to lift me off the ground.

But then again, nor can I make this out of toilet paper.

All in all, I'm hoping the WEIGHT will be worth it.

# Chapter 10

## GRAVITY SUCKS

... and thank goodness it does!

I learnt about **Sir Isaac Newton** and gravity at school. I learnt the bit I wrote about earlier — the apple story (which probably didn't actually happen to him).

I learnt that gravity is the force which keeps us on Earth, the Moon orbiting Earth, Earth orbiting the sun, the sun orbiting the galaxy (our galaxy is called the Milky Way), and so on for ever and ever and ever. Probably.

That's pretty mind blowing, isn't it? That's what got Kareem excited when we first talked about gravity. He gets into stuff like I do and has to read everything he can. So whilst I was learning about how the Saturn V was made to split apart, he was learning about gravity.

It's good to be part of a team. I started on this journey thinking I could do it all on my own, but the more I think about it, the more I realise I need other people.

The more people in a team, the stronger we are.

It's a bit like gravity!

The force of gravity is stronger when there's more **MASS** involved (REMEMBER: how much stuff is packed into an object). Something like an apple has a weaker gravity than something like Earth. So gravity is the force which pulls the apple to the ground, but it's also true to say that the apple pulls Earth up to it!

Without gravity, the universe would be a very different place. There would be nothing to keep planets spinning around stars, moons around planets, feet on the ground or crisps

in their packets. So jump up and down for gravity!

The reason I've been trying to learn about that whole rocket equation thing is because leaving Earth's gravitational pull is really, REALLY difficult. Like, even more difficult than getting out of bed in the morning. It requires thrust, which in turn requires a lot of fuel. But just as it was important to look at what mass is, so it will be important for me to look at what gravity is. In fact, the two things are closely connected because the greater an object's mass, the greater its gravitational influence will be.

To understand this we are going to sit beside Sir Isaac Newton, a man so clever his name is given over to entire branches (that's a tree joke — as in apple tree . . . oh, never mind) of physics: Newtonian motion, Newtonian mechanics, Newtonian fluids and more.

Isaac Newton, as you might remember, is the man who said for every action there is an equal and opposite reaction. I'm hoping to prove that by shooting hot exhaust gases **DOWNWARDS** in order to propel my spaceship **UPWARDS**. It's a reaction called **THRUST**, and another way of measuring this is in newtons. I'm going to stick with pounds for now though.

I can test Newton's law by filling a balloon with air and then letting go. The reason the balloon flies away is due to the thrust generated by the escaping air — the same as will happen with the exhaust from

my rocket (hopefully with more control over the direction).

So basically, I need to create the thrust by mixing kerosene or liquid hydrogen (which is better for the environment than kerosene) with oxygen and then sit back until it's time to land on the Moon. Simple.

Only . . . it isn't. Nothing ever is!

The true (ahem) gravity of the situation is that there are other forces in play here which are going to act against me.

One of the forces we have to overcome is the force of gravity.

Because of its mass (not size), Earth's gravitational force keeps us on the ground. It pulls things towards its centre. Luckily it isn't so strong as to prevent us from getting out of bed or taking a flight to another country. If Earth had enough mass, say the mass of a neutron star, then we could never move. I'm going to use this as an excuse next time Mum tells me to get out of bed.

And here's the surprising thing: you and I do the same! We pull each other and the planet towards us too. It's only because we have such little mass that nobody notices.

Isaac Newton wrote a law about gravity which said that force is proportional to an object's mass and that it is inversely proportional to the distance from that object's centre. This is called the **INVERSE SQUARE LAW**.

Wait, what does THAT mean?

What it means is that the greater the mass, the greater its gravity. Mass, remember, isn't the **SIZE** or **WEIGHT** of something but how much **STUFF** is packed into it. Newton's law also tells us that this force of gravity will become weaker the further away from the object (say, Earth) we are. If you are **TWICE** as far away then the effect gravity has on you (and you on it) becomes a **QUARTER**. Which is good! In fact, it's more than good. It's brilliant! It means the hardest part of my job is going to be getting into Earth orbit. And once I've done that, the rest is easy. Sort of. Maybe.

So now I understand why the Saturn V used so much fuel early on. It had to use two and a half stages just to get into orbit, because of Earth's gravity.

The other interesting thing about gravity

involves how a man called **Albert Einstein** improved Newton's law. It's this bit that makes it so much easier to understand orbits, whether we are talking about the Moon's orbit or a spaceship's.

Einstein figured out that not only does gravity affect objects, but it also affects space itself. The larger an object's mass, the more it affects space. In fact, it also affects time too, but let's save that thought for another ... time.

Here's a way to visualise what a large object like a planet or a star is doing to space with gravity because of its mass:

Ask four of your friends to hold a blanket between them. It's nice and flat, isn't it? Roll a tennis ball across and it will move from one

side to the other in a straight line. Now put
something heavy, say a bowling ball in the
centre. The ball creates a dip in the blanket. It's
warped space. Now roll the tennis ball across
and the ball will curve around the bowling ball.

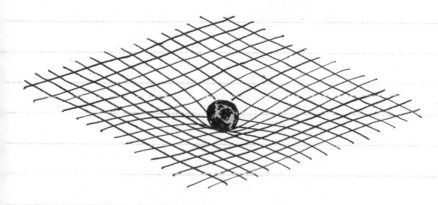

This simple example explains how the planets
move around the sun, how moons move around
planets and how I'm going to move around
Earth in my homemade Saturn V.

Or it will if I can get it into space in the first
place. At the moment it feels as though there's
a lot of theory going on and very little building.

I'm keen to crack on and start bending metal, but I know I have to learn WHY things work the way they do before I can build something so massive.

# Chapter 11

# TAKING A SPIN

It takes a lot of effort to get into space. And I'm not talking about the effort of deciding what clothes to pack. There's also the effort of burning enough fuel fast enough to create lift. Two-and-a-half stages of the Saturn V were given over to doing this because not only is there the mighty gravitational force to overcome but there is also **DRAG**.

The faster something moves through the

air, the more drag is generated. Take a walk and you might feel your hair move even if there's no breeze. But take a ride in an open-topped car and your hair will be swept back much harder because of the drag (not the wind). If you ride on a roller-coaster then the drag will cause even your cheeks to be pushed back.

In a similar way as the rocket pushes against the air, the air pushes back against the rocket (equal and opposite reactions, remember). The bigger the rocket, the bigger this effect

becomes. A smaller rocket would produce less drag but couldn't produce the thrust I need to reach space.

But I've learnt that there is a sweet spot which helps me overcome the drag and the gravity. It's called **ESCAPE VELOCITY**.

For now, I'm only trying to figure out how to escape into low Earth orbit. To do this, I need to travel at **7 km/s**. That's a face-flattening **TWENTY** times the speed of sound. But I'm going to trust the maths. I'm going to trust the rocket equation. I know how much fuel it will take to get me there because the maths has told me what thrust I need to generate in order to reach this speed.

Another way to think of getting into orbit is that I'll need to go fast enough in order to fall around Earth.

Huh?

**Douglas Adams**, the brilliant writer of some very funny books, wrote this about flying:

"Flying is learning how to throw yourself at the ground and miss."

That is exactly what happens. Flying is falling. The spaceship will be falling but it will fall around Earth's curve. That's an orbit, and orbits are the name we give to the way things move around other things. Like the Moon around Earth, Earth around the sun, and my spaceship (at least for a while) around Earth.

Sir Isaac Newton had a similar example. He asked us to imagine standing on top of a mountain and firing a cannon. If it was fired at a slow speed then the cannonball would travel in a straight line until it ran out of energy and fell to Earth. You can try this just by throwing a tennis ball.

Throw the ball and see how it falls to the ground in an arc. It won't fly in a straight line then drop straight down.

If you throw your tennis ball hard enough then it will still fall in an arc, but Earth's surface would curve beneath it and the ball would fall right round to where it began.

Before Newton, in the early **1600s,** a man named **Johannes Kepler** wrote three laws to describe planetary motion. First, he said planets moved in elliptical orbits. Earth moves in an ellipse around the sun. It's not a really squashed sort of ellipse though, but it's not a circle either. At its closest (this is called **PERIGEE**), Earth comes within **91,500,000 miles** of the sun. And at its furthest (this is called **APOGEE**), Earth is **94,500,000 miles** from the sun.

Perigee apogee. Perigee apogee. It's like a spell from Harry Potter!

It is possible to get into a circular orbit but it's the elliptical orbit which will be useful to me when I get into space.

And the reason for that is described in Kepler's second law.

Kepler's second law describes how a planet (or my spaceship) covers equal areas in equal times.

Here's a diagram to explain this:

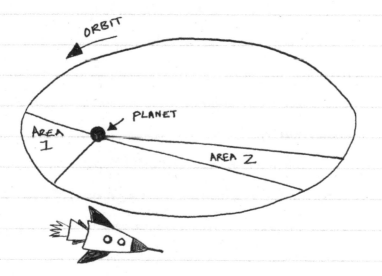

**Area one** in this diagram is equal to **area two**. My speed will change depending upon where along that orbital curve I am.

I will go fastest when I'm at perigee to Earth (closest) and slowest when I'm at apogee to Earth (furthest).

So look at the diagram again. It will take me **EQUALLY** as long a time to travel past area one as it does past area two.

Why does this matter? Because this process is what will keep me in orbit and provide the energy to do so. In other words, I don't need to be firing my engines just to keep travelling around Earth.

All this is thanks to **GRAVITY** pulling at the spaceship (or the planet, or the moon). Objects WANT to go in a straight line and if there was no gravity then that's exactly what they'd do. But if I can get to the right height above Earth then gravity will give me the energy to keep in orbit.

That's great, but I can't just stick around

in Earth orbit. I have a moon to get to. And to do that I need to find a way to get into something called **trans-lunar injection**.

And that isn't as painful as it sounds.

# Chapter 12

# I WANT TO BREAK FREE

The record for remaining in space stands at **437 days** and was set by the Russian cosmonaut, **Valeri Polyakov**. That was back in **1995** onboard the **Mir space station**. As proud as I'll be for getting into Earth orbit, I don't plan on staying there.

To get my spaceship out of Earth orbit and towards the Moon, I have to perform something called a **trans-lunar injection**.

In other words, I need to inject my spaceship into a path between Earth and the Moon.

In my head, this is like playing netball but another way to think of it is to say that I'll be changing my orbit.

Thankfully, if everything has gone to plan, I'll still have half the third stage of my spaceship to provide the fuel to do this. Firing the third stage is exactly what the Apollo astronauts did in order to escape the pull of Earth's gravity and send them flying towards the Moon.

Now, there are two MORE things I need to learn about.

The first thing is that if I want a way to go faster without wasting a huge amount of fuel, I'll need to get closer to the planet. This is part of how orbital mechanics work. Orbital mechanics are not the overall-wearing, wrench-carrying people who might be waiting for me in space if I need to change a part on my spaceship. It's simply the science of how rockets interact with gravity, including how different height orbits work.

If I need to slow down, then I have to get into a higher orbit.

This is all part of something called the **conservation of angular momentum,** or how energy behaves when it's in motion around an object.

The second thing I need to learn about is not surprising and it's this: the Moon is moving.

I'm a genius of the spectacularly obvious. Next lesson: water is wet. It is important to mention this because it means I can't just point my spaceship at the Moon and fire my engines. If I did, then the Moon wouldn't be where it was by the time I reached it. This isn't going to be like flying to Spain.

The Moon's orbit is almost (but not quite) circular and it takes about **twenty-seven days** for it to go around Earth once. I'm wishing it travelled along a fixed path because then everything would be so much easier. I mean, look at this diagram!

It's exaggerated but it shows how the Moon's orbit changes every **eight years**.

So yeah, NOTHING is simple.

The good news is that whilst the Moon and Earth (and me) are all moving, there are at least **200,000,000,000 stars in the Milky Way**

(our galaxy) which are so far away as to appear stationary. Having fixed points in the sky means we can set a course in the way sailors would have done hundreds of years ago. This is called **CELESTIAL NAVIGATION**.

It's highly unlikely that the Moon will suddenly change direction, so once I get on the correct path (or 'trajectory', as it's called) then my journey will be a lot easier. To calculate how to get on that correct path I must understand three things: **pitch, yaw and roll**.

Let's picture an aeroplane to help with this.

Imagine the plane side on. The **PITCH** is the up or down angle it flies along (so whether the nose is pointing upwards and downwards).

Now imagine the plane top down. The **YAW** is the amount it's twisted left or right.

And finally, look at the plane face on from the front. The **ROLL** is the amount it tilts one way or the other.

I have to learn how to steer my spaceship along each axis.

And that's 'just' to fly! To fly in the right direction I must learn even more.

To find the Moon I will have to measure the angles between a star and the Moon's horizon using a device called a sextant. I'll feed those numbers into the computer (yes, I need to build my own computer too, but we will get to that later). The computer will tell me how much pitch, yaw and roll I need in order to stay on the right trajectory.

Here's another thing though: I will need to do this a lot because I'm not aiming for where the Moon **IS** but where it **WILL BE**. If I plan properly then I won't need many changes to my course.

By this point in my journey I will have used all the fuel in each of my Saturn V's three major rocket stages. I've already ditched stages one and two so now it's time to say goodbye to stage three.

Stage three is as empty as a bag of sweets three seconds after they're opened. If this was a bag of sweets then I'd find a litter bin, but there are no bins in space so I'm going to have to just abandon it. It's sad because there is a lot of junk in orbit now and this is becoming a problem and a potential danger to future missions.

Before I can get rid of stage three I must first turn the **Command and Service Module** (called the CSM) around and dock with the **Lunar Module**. Then I will pull it away from the stage three section whilst moving at high speed towards the Moon.

As small and simple as it looks, the **Command Module** (or rather, the **Service Module** part of it) packs a decent amount of thrust power. It has an engine which can put me into, and take me out of, lunar orbit. It also has a **reaction control system**. That's a fancy name for the thrusters which can sort all that pitch, yaw and roll stuff out. It looks pretty weird (like a stubby pencil) but it's still amazing.

Also, it's worth saying that because out in space I won't be fighting huge gravitational or air friction forces, a little power will go a long way.

And oh dear, oh dear, what a long way it is.

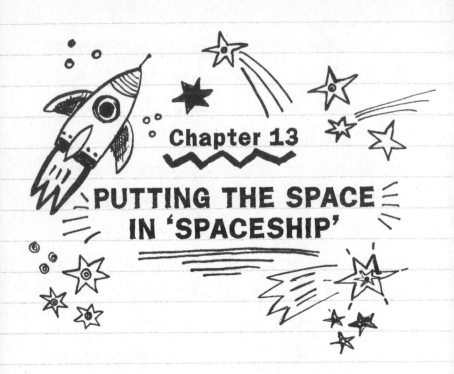

# Chapter 13

# PUTTING THE SPACE IN 'SPACESHIP'

Almost every part of the Saturn V was designed to work in an atmosphere as well as in space. That's why it's shaped the way it is. So in some ways the Saturn V isn't just a spaceship.

There's one bit which was designed to only work in space. This makes it the spaciest spaceship there is.

I'm talking about the **Lunar Module**, the

craft which will take me down on to the Moon's surface.

I made one in Lego as a way to learn more about how it works and why it looks the way it does.

I'm looking forward to building this most of all. I love it, for reasons which will become obvious, and I know that when I've tightened the last nut and bolt on its funny-shaped frame, I'll sit back and feel proud.

By the time I come to fly in it, I will have pulled the little spaceship out from the third stage and flown the rest of the way to the Moon with it connected to the Command and Service Module. While it's attached, I shall be able to move between the two via the docking hatch. There's more space in the Lunar Module, and I need to be in there anyway once I start my descent.

Everything is perfect. Everything except . . . how it looks.

It's like a cross between a spider and a portable toilet. It looks so fragile, so clearly made from aluminium foil and scaffolding. When I started on this project I thought it couldn't possibly fly in space.

I was wrong. REALLY wrong.

I now know that the **LM** (the Lunar Module, which everyone called the 'LEM' because an earlier name for it had been the **lunar excursion module**) had two engines: one for descent and one for the ascent. Thanks to some really smart design which meant it could save fuel, the LM would leave the descent part behind.

The Lunar Module was a true spaceship, designed to only ever fly in space. Because of that, it did not need engines capable of battling with Earth's gravity or an outer skin capable

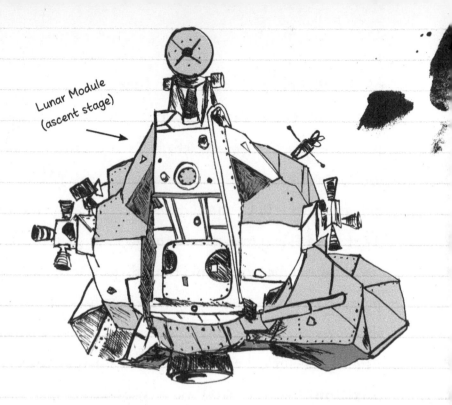

Lunar Module
(ascent stage)

of protecting against our atmosphere. It didn't
need the aerodynamics you'd need in a plane or
a car in order to reduce drag and slip through
the air. But if you're thinking (like I did) that it
was a clunky old thing, then prepare to be a bit
amazed.

Rather than being a flying toilet, the LM
handled like a jet plane and could reach speeds

of **5,900 km/h**. That's more than five times the speed of sound; pretty impressive for a vehicle whose walls were, in some places, just **0.1 mm** thick!  That's like flying in a cake wrapper!

Now, maybe you think that it just sort of plopped down on to the lunar surface. WRONG (don't worry, I was wrong on all of this too). The LM actually began flying in a **horizontal position** (on its side) nine kilometres high and was rotated in order for the pilot (**Neil Armstrong** in the case of **Apollo 11**) to see the surface. Only once it had dropped lower did it settle into the familiar landing position we see in photos.

Even though lifting off from the Moon won't take anywhere near as much thrust, I'm still going to have to take steps to keep the weight down to a minimum. That's why my lunar module was designed to leave its landing stage behind, and it's even why I won't be needing seats.

Yes, you read that right. Where we're going we don't need chairs.

The original design included them but at some point, someone asked why and everyone else was all, like, good point! They must have remembered that the lower gravity up there (or down there, there is no up or down in space) meant chairs were a bit pointless.

Astronauts sleep in sleeping bags but these can be on the ceiling, floor or walls of the spaceship. They will strap themselves in only to stop from floating away and getting a big toe stuck up the nose of their fellow astronauts. There's not enough gravity to keep them lying down in the sense we do here on Earth. So really, they won't sit either. Losing them made for a lighter spaceship.

It is all so clever, and nothing like what science-fiction movies taught me to expect. So there's no way on Earth (or Moon) I'm going to start redesigning anything just because it doesn't look like an X-Wing and my friends might laugh at me.

If it ain't broke, don't fix it. During the Apollo missions, the Saturn V rockets were responsible for taking **twenty-four men** to the Moon and the Lunar Modules put **twelve** of those on it. From where I'm standing, that totally counts as 'ain't broke'.

OK. So it can't have escaped your notice that, with the exception of a matchstick rocket, buying some space food and making a home carbon dioxide scrubber, I haven't done anything in the way of actually building my own Saturn V.

Well, grab your welding torches because it's time I spoke to some people who can get me started.

AT LAST!

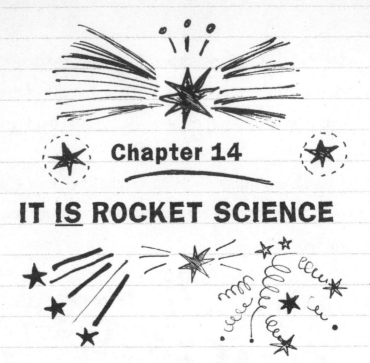

## Chapter 14

# IT <u>IS</u> ROCKET SCIENCE

The only person at my school who remembers the Moon landing is Mr Whittaker. He jokes that he's over a hundred years old and even remembers the first train. And the first sandwich.

At least, I think he's joking.

I asked him how easy it is to copy old stuff and he said that it depends on the stuff. Kareem blurted out that we were building a spaceship. I glared at him, but Mr Whittaker didn't laugh

and said he believed we could do anything we set our minds to.

That was a really nice thing to say but the more I learn, the more I realise this is a lot harder than I expected it to be.

In theory, it all seems simple. Remember my Lunar List? The one where I said I need to build the rocket, fill it with fuel and then ignite the engines? I need to look into a few things (spacesuits and mission control being two of them) and I still think that with the right blueprints, an understanding of orbital mechanics and a decent connection to YouTube for tutorial videos on my journey then, it has to be possible, but . . . easy?

I don't think so.

The Saturn V had over **3,000,000 parts** to it. Even if I make this thing using Lego then it still won't be easy to build.

Which isn't the same as saying it's impossible though, right?

A few of us (Kareem was there, and so were the twins) got to go on a science visit. We did some experiments and met some people who built rockets. Like, proper rockets. I didn't reveal my master plan to them but I did ask a few questions.

"Start small," they told me.

So I did. I looked online and found a kit to get me started. It was only a small one, capable of reaching a few hundred feet into the air. There are bigger ones which could fly to just below the area where aeroplanes travel, but I don't get enough pocket money for one of those.

Kareem says I'd need special permission anyway. Is leaving Earth like leaving the country?

Will I need a passport? Or a letter from the Queen? I mean, a rocket zipping in front of an aeroplane on its way to Alicante could cause problems, and I don't want to be chased by the Space Force police.

But seriously though — if my spaceship exploded, then it would do a LOT of damage to anything around.

The last thing I need is to set off a major international incident and have people in black suits and dark glasses turning up at my house and carrying me off to prison.

If you think back to the basics of how a rocket works, I discovered that it's a controlled explosion. I mix the fuel (kerosene or liquid hydrogen) with the oxygen and then ignite.

A rocket is a bit like a firework. Even though they are tested and tested and tested some more, things can and do go wrong.

Elon Musk's very impressive **SpaceX** company built a reusable rocket called the **Falcon**. The stages work like mine will, but with a BIG difference. When the Falcon has finished with a stage and reached a set altitude, the stage breaks away and lands itself . . . **ON A FLOATING PLATFORM**. That's mind-bogglingly, eye-poppingly brilliant. To get that to work, SpaceX spent millions and millions of dollars and there were a LOT of explosions because it didn't always work the first time.

I know space flight will never be **100% safe** but according to **Wernher von Braun**, one of the masterminds behind the Apollo mission, the Saturn V used on the Apollo 4 test was **99.999% reliable**. We will soon see how that isn't as great as it sounds.

For now, though, I'm going to have to talk

to the right people, including the fire brigade, but I reckon I can trust NASA's testing and try out the rocket kit I'd bought to get a feel for when I'd strap myself into my very own Saturn V.

I'm glad I tried this out with small rockets though. Kareem and I made our match rocket and then I bought the kit to make a bigger one. And so I want to tell you about what happened when I launched that on a cloudy day. I realised there was something I couldn't control.

# Chapter 15

## WHETHER THE WEATHER WILL HOLD

We were all stuck inside today at school. It rained so much even the trees were covering their heads.

Yesterday was the sunniest, hottest day so nobody really expected this.

I also didn't expect it to be windy when I launched my little rocket but a gust came out of nowhere and it was all . . .

# 5 . . . 4 . . . 3 . . . 2 . . . GONE!

My poor rocket shot up in the sky and then sort of went sideways and then spun around and disappeared into the trees.

As I searched, a question popped into my head: "Will the weather affect my Saturn V?"

The **five F-1 engines** of the first stage are really powerful. They produce **7,600,000 pounds** of thrust so how can a bit of wind blow such a powerful rocket off course?

Loads of rocket launches have been cancelled because of bad weather — even when the sky looks pretty clear.

I can understand cancelling due to the risk of a lightning storm. When **Apollo 12** launched, it

caused lightning to strike
the spacecraft and set
off every alarm in the
Command Module. Fuel
cells were taken offline

and the ship had to rely on
batteries. These wouldn't have provided enough
power and the mission was almost aborted
except for the quick thinking of two people:
**John Aaron**, back in Mission Control, and **Alan
Bean**, onboard Apollo 12. Aaron remembered a
switch which could be used to provide backup
power. Unfortunately, mission commander Pete
Conrad didn't know where that switch was
(there are a LOT of switches on the panel so
I'm going to have to learn each and every one
of them). Luckily, Alan Bean did, flipped it, and
the mission continued to the Moon.

What the crew weren't told at the time

was that the lightning strike might also have caused a problem with the parachute. The parachute is supposed to come out during re-entry and without it, the Command Module would be travelling too fast and so crash into the Pacific Ocean. There was no point in telling the crew this; Mission Control decided that they may as well enjoy the flight to the Moon. Fortunately for everyone, the parachute did work and they all returned to Earth safely.

But listen: the science of how a rocket can attract lightning is pretty awesome. In a scary kind of way.

Large objects (trees, buildings, giant rockets) can be struck by lightning. When this happens, the object can be seriously damaged.

But lightning is electricity. And so if it can find a wire to jump down then it will. The trick is to find a way to get rid of that electricity in a safe way. If the wire goes into the ground then the lightning will rush down the wire and discharge safely.

This is why a tall building will often have a lightning rod — a long bit of metal stretching above the building. The rod is connected to a thick wire which runs down the building and into the ground. So instead of striking the building, the lightning races down the rod.

This is called the **path of least resistance**.

That's right, lightning is lazy! This process is called '**conducting**' and a lightning rod is also called a **lightning conductor**. The reason a building might want to attract it is to control where the strike occurs and deal with it. Without the conductor, the lightning could damage other parts.

A rocket in the sky can also act as a conductor. Even more importantly, the exhaust is partly **ionised**. That means the **electrons** in the exhaust fumes are acting like a long wire to the ground. But unlike the lightning rod, which is a simple path with nothing for lightning to damage on its way down, a rocket has lots of electronics, all of which are under threat until the lightning goes away.

So yes, the weather can make a

**BIG DIFFERENCE!**

The thing about the wind is that the rocket is designed to overcome the drag of air resistance. As a rocket travels upwards, the air pushes down. All of this is accounted for in the rocket equation and the thrust we generate (all **7,600,000 pounds** of it) will deal with it. Except for if the conditions are unpredictable. A change in direction of the wind can and will cause major problems.

And it's not just wind and lightning I need to worry about! Even the **temperature** can affect my rocket.

Another reason why weather conditions have to be more or less perfect is that problems can occur if it gets too cold. A build up of ice will damage a spaceship.

In **1986**, the Space Shuttle '**Challenger**' exploded just over a minute after launch.

Seven astronauts died.

An investigation into the cause found that some of the rubber seals between sections of the rocket boosters had failed because rubber doesn't work well at low temperatures. Remember, I need to keep my liquid oxygen from mixing with my kerosene until exactly the right moment. The failure of the Space Shuttle's seals was due to the cold weather and it caused a chain reaction which destroyed the spaceship.

Maths Time!

My Saturn V will have over **3,000,000** parts to it. To make the numbers easier let's call it exactly **3,000,000**.

If I say I'm **99%** certain of success then

you might feel pretty confident and be happy to strap yourself in next to me. 1% seems hardly worth caring about.

But let's work out what **1%** of **3,000,000** really means.

To get **1%** of **3,000,000** I have to do this sum:

**3,000,000 ÷ 100**

The answer is **30,000**. In other words, if I say that I'm **99%** certain of all the parts in my spaceship then there are still **30,000** parts which could go wrong.

**THIRTY-THOUSAND.**
**GULP!**

For Challenger, it took just **one part** to go wrong and **seven people** died.

That's a big number and a terrible consequence. I'll be honest here, I'm starting to have second thoughts. But whilst I have them, I'm going to learn about the other spaceship I'll need to build. And it's a much smaller spaceship.

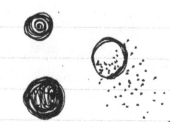

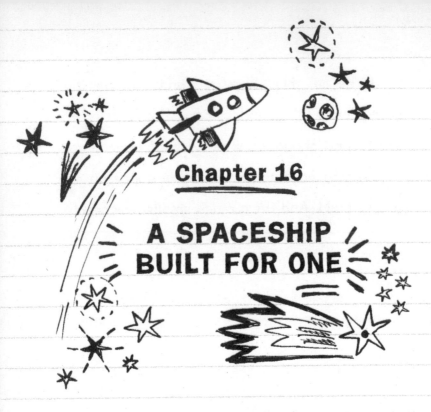

# Chapter 16

## A SPACESHIP BUILT FOR ONE

I showed Kareem a film of Neil Armstrong and Buzz Aldrin putting the United States flag on the Moon. Then I asked him how many spaceships he could see.

He said one and I said NO! He was only looking at the Lunar Module.

The answer is three. There are three spaceships. There is the Lunar Module AND the two spaceships worn by the astronauts.

Kareem said get out, but it's true!

A spacesuit is a spaceship. It might not have any engines (although some do) but it's still a spaceship. And it will keep me alive in space.

I already own a spacesuit but that one wouldn't keep me dry in a shower, let alone let me breathe in space. I wear it at Hallowe'en, and sometimes to birthday parties. No, I do not care who knows I'm a space nerd.

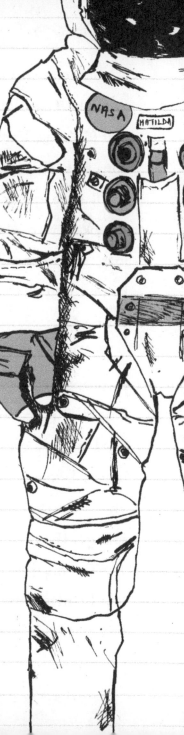

145

You can buy more realistic spacesuits which look like the real thing, but don't be fooled: if you (OK, me, I made this mistake) think you (I) can just put it on and do a spacewalk, then you'll be a goner. ME! I'll be a goner. I'm glad I looked into this because I thought that as long as the seals between the gloves/boots/helmet and the rest of the suit were tight then I'd be OK.

If it were ONLY that simple. But it isn't. A proper spacesuit is made from over sixty layers of material.

I haven't even got sixty items of clothing — unless I count my socks — but imagine wearing that many layers! No wonder astronauts look as though they can hardly bend!

The layers help keep the air inside so that I can breathe. And remember, even the breathing bit is going to be complicated.

Think back to when I was learning about what type of air I'd need to breathe in my spaceship. I discovered that I could breathe **pure oxygen** (which is light and so needs less effort from the rocket to lift it along with me). BUT I can only breathe pure oxygen if the air pressure is a lot lower than I'm used to on Earth.

I need to learn a bit more about this because the level of air pressure in my spacesuit is important.

LIKE, REALLY IMPORTANT.

This is what I've learnt.

If I take a pan of water and put it on a small camp stove then I can time how long it takes for the water to boil.

If I climb a mountain and boil that pan of water on the camp stove again, then I'll find the water boils much more quickly on the mountain than it does at home.

That's because the air pressure on top of a mountain is a lot lower than it is at sea level. It's why you can never have a good cup of tea on a mountain because the water won't be hot enough. So that's interesting, isn't it? Boiling doesn't mean the same as hot.

Why does this matter?

It matters because in space there is **no air pressure** (it's a **vacuum**, remember). That means the boiling point of water in space is much, much lower. In fact it's about **0°C.** And guess what has a lot of water? Our bodies do, that's what.

So without a spacesuit, all the water in my body would boil and freeze at the same time.

Of course, I wouldn't be able to breathe either. A proper spacesuit is really important!

Before I move on, I'll just tell you something else I've read about. The temperature at which water boils in space is called a '**triple point**'. The triple point of something is when the solid, liquid and gas states ALL exist at the same temperature. Different substances have different triple points (and different boiling points). And on that subject it also tells me that to keep my hydrogen (which I need for the second and third stage fuels) liquid I must store it at **-253°C**. That is, if the atmospheric pressure is the same as on Earth. I can change the temperature point (making it easier to keep liquid) if I increase the pressure. BUT, as with everything on this project, that brings dangers too.

I mentioned all this to Kareem and he scratched his head and said maybe I should give up.

I'm not going to, but it is getting tricky. Making a spaceship isn't just a case of copying the blueprints.

Anyhooooooo . . . back to my spacesuit.

I'll be breathing oxygen, so the pressure in my suit needs to be about the same as it is in my spaceship.

But can you remember what I need to remove if I'm breathing in an airtight space like a spacesuit or spaceship? That's right, **carbon dioxide**! I was going to do this on my spaceship by using an aquarium pump and a lemonade bottle filled with water and algae. Being honest, I'm not so sure I'd trust this method in a spacesuit. Perhaps it's time to buy some **lithium hydroxide canisters** like the ones used for the Apollo missions.

And then maybe I can breathe easy.

Or maybe not, because Kareem just sent me a text to ask me how I'm going to keep cool.

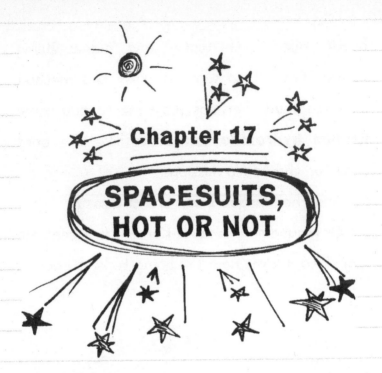

# Chapter 17

## SPACESUITS, HOT OR NOT

"Kareem," I said! "What are you talking about? There's no weather in space. There aren't cloudy days and rainy days. There's zero chance of snow. In fact, there's more chance of being hit by a floating meatball than a snowball. I'm going to be all snug in my spacesuit."

Only, it's more complicated than that. OF COURSE it is!

It always is.

There may be no cloudy days but there is a sun. Our closest star, shining away some **93,000,000 miles** away. With no atmosphere (with all its clouds and air currents) to keep that sun in check, temperatures in space are something to worry about.

For astronauts living and working on the International Space Station it's either super hot or super cold. And this changes every **forty-five minutes**.

It takes the ISS **ninety minutes** to complete a single Earth orbit. Depending upon the path it's on, that means it can face the sun for half that time or even all that time.

During this time, the temperature can rise to a shirt-drenching **121°C**. At other times, the temperature can drop to **-157°C** — enough to make a polar bear reach for an extra coat.

So OK, Kareem is right. How am I going to keep cool? And warm? At the same time.

Easy. I just need to create a microclimate, my own little world, wherever I am.

OK, that doesn't sound so easy.

I must find a way of stopping anything outside the suit affecting anything inside the suit.

This is how a fridge works. I just need to make sure the temperature on the inside isn't as cold as a fridge otherwise my tongue will turn into an ice lolly.

It also means every bit of the suit is as important as every other bit — from the backpack to the gloves.

If I go out on a cold day I've noticed that the bits of me which get coldest fastest are my fingertips, my ears and my nose. The warmest bit of me is my chest. That's because my body is keeping my heart warm because that's the most important part of me. There's no point having lovely warm fingers and toes if my heart is frozen solid!

I don't want frozen fingers, though. I can't flick switches or turn handles or open doors very easily if I have frozen fingers. My gloves will need little heaters inside them. Like I said, every bit is important.

So let me look at each bit of the suit and see what it does and why.

The gloves slot into the arms which in turn slot into a solid body section (like a suit of armour). The body section can also be called the torso shell — which mustn't be confused with a tortoise shell.

There is a section for the lower half of my body too, with enough flexibility so I can bend my legs and walk about. It's all very bulky, and moving isn't easy, but there's no way I'd swap it for my swimming costume.

Every part is made up of layer upon layer of material. There are layers to protect against tiny meteorites, and layers which are waterproof, fireproof and cold-proof, air-proof, and so on. I'm not sure whether they are childproof but I suppose I'll find out. There are layers for the liquid cooling which will run around my body, and a layer to keep my body at the correct atmospheric pressure. When I'm suited up, I'll be like a walking Thermos flask.

It's all incredibly well designed and there's no way my fancy-dress spacesuit (£14.99 online) is up to the job. If I'm going to do this then I need to do it properly — right down to the last detail.

The backpack is the most complicated bit. I sort of always knew it was more than somewhere to keep my sandwiches but I never realised just how much is packed in there. In fact, there's so much packed in that I won't have room for my sandwiches.

The proper name for the backpack is the **Personal Life Support System**, or PLSS. Every bit of the spacesuit is important, but this bit is the super-most-really-really important bit.

The PLSS contains oxygen tanks and a fan which keeps the air moving through my suit. It also contains scrubbers to remove the carbon dioxide when I breathe out. I'll feel like I'm going deep-sea diving! In fact, spacesuits do get tested underwater. I'd rather discover a leak whilst standing in a swimming pool than hear the hiss of escaping air when I'm walking on the Moon.

I'm just getting started. There's a lot more to the Personal Life Support System to learn about.

I compared my spacesuit to a fridge and

there is a function in the PLSS which keeps water cool. I'll need to wear a special undergarment which is lined with tubes to carry this cooled water all around me. That keeps me from getting too hot and the PLSS makes sure it keeps on pumping. The undergarment also has vents for my sweat to drip through. Then my sweat gets recycled into the water cooling system.

There is one liquid which I won't be recycling in my spacesuit. My wee will be absorbed in the 'maximum absorption garment' (otherwise known as a nappy).

Yucky but, strange as this might seem, if I could recycle my wee then I would. Every drop of water is precious out in space and the more I can recycle, the longer I can stay there and the less I need to carry.

Let's not forget the helmet. Not just a window to appreciate the calm beauty of the cosmos or something to catch my snot when I sneeze, the helmet has the ability to direct the flow of oxygen to my face and keep it at exactly the right pressure.

My PLSS has to keep all the spacesuit functions monitored (and I can check on that using a special wrist mirror which lets me look and use the control panel on my chest). I'll even have a radio onboard, not to listen to music but to talk with the people back on Earth.

People?

I'd sort of forgotten about people.

# Chapter 18

# HOUSTON, WE HAVE A PROBLEM

We really do. Or at least, I do.

So far I've tried to look into how I'm going to build my spaceship and how to get it into space (and to the Moon). I still need to figure out how to make all **3,000,000 parts** but there's a huge element I've been trying to ignore: people.

I thought I'd need three people to fly the spaceship. (I was thinking of asking Kareem but he said he's busy with something else, so maybe I'll ask the twins.) The Command Module and the Lunar Module were designed to be managed by three. Two people will travel down to the Moon in the LM whilst the other stays behind in the CM, orbiting around and around until the moonwalkers are ready to rendezvous again.

So three should be OK, right?

Wrong.

Flying the Saturn V wasn't (and can't be) just a three-person job. In fact, some of the Apollo astronauts felt that being an experienced pilot wasn't necessary because so much of the flying was done

NASA astronaut pin

by people other than the onboard crew. Whilst that's great for me, because I'm about as inexperienced as it's possible to get, it does mean that someone else must be doing most of the flying.

Two words:

**MISSION CONTROL**

It took thousands of men and women on Earth to get three men to the Moon. There were **scientists, engineers, instructors, designers, inspectors** and so many more that the list could almost stretch into space! Mission Control was the hub of activity and was operated night and day for the duration of each Apollo mission.

The people in Mission Control oversaw every

part of the epic journey, keeping an eye on how the rocket was performing, the crew's health, how the computers were handling operations and much more. This wasn't a case of having people stand over the astronaut's shoulders whilst they did the flying, the staff back on Earth were vital to the success. When the Saturn V needed to shift orbits from Earth to Lunar, the calculations were done back at Mission Control. How much and for how long an engine needs to be fired for is as complicated as it is important.

I know I can make use of a much better computer system than the one used back in 1969, but even so, I'm not sure that three people can manage everything.

That's brought me back down to Earth. With a bump.

One of the ways in which the Saturn V

rockets found their way to the Moon was by talking to Mission Control. NASA could follow the position and velocity (that's the speed and path the rocket was taking) by using a network of

People I can ask to help

Pilots: Me, Chitra, Basil

Ground Crew: Mum, Dad, Mr Birch, Aunty Con, Phil (maybe), Cat.

Might have to ask Gran.

Earth-based communication stations. They kept an eye on how long it took for signals to first reach, and then return from, the spaceship. Using that information they could work out where in space the astronauts were.

And can you remember the problem with Apollo 13? The scrubbers which would keep the air breathable needed to be changed. The crew were living in the Lunar Module but it didn't have enough scrubbers to last the journey.

The Command Module did but those wouldn't fit into the Lunar Module's systems. It was a square peg/round hole sort of problem.

So guess who figured out the solution?

That's right, the folk back in Mission Control.

Imagine having to sit an exam, a really big and important one. Wouldn't it be great if each time you got stuck you could just stick your hand in the air and ask one of the thousands of people around to help with the answer?

That's what Mission Control could and did do for the Apollo astronauts.

Just like our school needs the headteacher and governors and all the parents to help out, so each mission needed Mission Control. Those people worked really hard to make sure the crew got to the Moon and arrived back safely.

And that's yet another thing: who is going to collect me once I splash down in the Pacific

Ocean? I'm not sure I can call a taxi whilst bobbing about in my Command Module. To top off my fear of heights, I'll add that I'm not great on the sea either. You'll find me being sick in a carrier bag from the NASA gift shop.

Suddenly, even the fact that this is fifty-year-old technology isn't enough to keep me going on this project.

I need to sit down and think about this a little bit more.

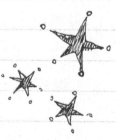

# Chapter 19

## CHIPS WITH EVERYTHING

I sent a sad face emoji to Kareem. He sent me a link to an ancient video game called Jetpac, which has an astronaut building a spaceship, and said maybe I should stick to games. I replied with eight more sad faces.

Building a Saturn V isn't as easy as I first thought. I've learnt loads though. I know about gravity and vacuums and orbits and air pressure and so much more. So that's good. But maybe Kareem is right. He knows that the bit I've been looking forward to the most is the computer bit.

He said he thinks I shouldn't worry about what I can't do and that I should talk about what I love most. Just like when Mrs Hulme told him to talk about science instead of poetry.

So I'm going to talk about computers.

I love computers. I love how they work and I love using Scratch to code games. I know that my computer is far more  powerful than the ones used to send astronauts to the Moon. Which doesn't mean computers back then were rubbish. In fact, the way they were used was nothing short of incredible and a great deal of that was down to a lady called **Margaret Hamilton**.

Margaret Hamilton led the team which programmed the computers on the Command Module and the Lunar Module. By the standards of today they were basic and yet they still made it possible  for the astronauts to land on the Moon.

When I talk about the Apollo mission computers, I don't mean the sort of computer I'm using to write this book. This one has a screen and access to the Internet. Computers back in the **1960s** had buttons with numbers on (like a calculator) and a series of labels which would light up depending on what was happening in the spaceship. The screen could only display numbers or a few pre-set words — like we see on microwave ovens today. But it was still the most advanced computer of its time and was absolutely vital in getting people to the Moon, and the computer program was really clever.

At a very basic level, computer programs keep track of electrical signals coming into it. The programmer (like Margaret Hamilton) will have told the computer what each signal means. If it has a signal coming in from a button press, the computer program will recognise which button has been pressed because the electrical signal will be different to all the other button signals. The program then acts upon that signal. It might switch a light on or start an engine or sound an alarm.

The computers on board the Command and Lunar Modules had **4k of memory** for the astronauts to use and store instructions (called RAM) and **32k of memory** where fixed programs were stored (this is called ROM).

To give you an idea of the numbers here, let's look at the words I'm using.

A **'k'** is a **kilobyte**. **1 kilobyte** is another way of saying **1,024 bytes**. **1 byte** is made up of **8 bits**. A bit is either a **1** or a **0**, like a switch which says I'm on or off. That's the basic instruction of any computer.

| 128 | 64 | 32 | 16 | 8 | 4 | 2 | 1 |
|-----|----|----|----|----|----|----|----|
| 0 | 1 | 0 | 1 | 0 | 0 | 0 | 1 |

= 81

Doing sums in binary. Each column is either ON (1) or OFF (0)

There are **1,024 kilobytes** in **1 megabyte**. When you take a photo, your phone will store that and use maybe half a megabyte of data (which is **512k**). Now let's think bigger. There are **1,024 megabytes** in a **gigabyte**. A basic

172

phone in **2021** can store **8 gigabytes**. My laptop can store **512 gigabytes** and I keep lots of photos, music, apps and documents on it but, I'm running out of space. I'd really like **1 terabyte**, or even 2. There are **1,024 gigabytes** in a single **terabyte**.

I'll say this again: the Apollo computers had

**4 KILOBYTES.**

If I describe **2 terabytes** in **kilobytes** then I'd say it has **2,000,000,000 kilobytes** (OK, that's not quite true because it's in multiples of 1,024 but it's easier to understand than looking at 2,048,000,000,000 or whatever).

But even with just **4k** (or **26k** including the non-changeable memory), the computers could still keep track of lots of different systems, checking the electrical signals coming in and responding according to how the program said it should.

Neil Armstrong and Buzz Aldrin might have crashed on the Moon if it weren't for the computer.

Apollo's onboard computer

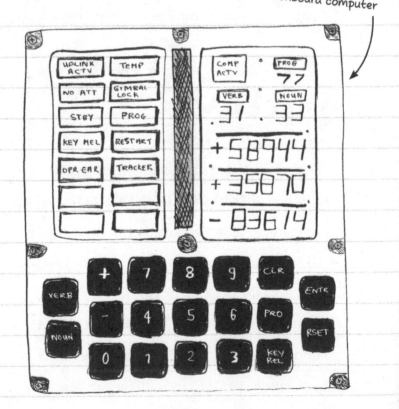

When the **Apollo 11 Lunar Module**, named **The Eagle**, was coming down, an alarm sounded. There were so many problems that the computer was struggling to keep up. It had noticed that the information coming in from the Lunar Module was patchy. Radar data to tell it where and how high they were was faulty. They were also travelling too fast.

Thanks to the warnings from the computer, Buzz Aldrin could check their descent himself and Neil Armstrong could try to land manually.

Even so, they almost didn't make it. Travelling too fast meant that the safe landing spot everyone back at Mission Control had decided would be perfect was now far behind them. Armstrong had to find a new place to park but he was running out of fuel.

The Lunar Module hurtled past crater after crater and the fuel warnings sounded again and

again. Buzz called out the numbers but Neil kept his eye on the Moon as the lengthening shadow of their spaceship told them they were getting lower and lower.

And then, with fifteen seconds worth of fuel remaining, Neil Armstrong switched off the engine.

**THE EAGLE HAD LANDED.**

One of the reasons the Lunar Module had overshot the original landing zone and set off the alarm was because the communications between Apollo and Earth had become unreliable on the descent and information wasn't getting through.

As clever as the onboard computers were, they didn't do all the work. That was down to the much more complicated deep space network back on Earth. Yes, you guessed it, Mission Control was in charge.

It looks as though I won't be able to build a spaceship and fly to the Moon by myself after all.

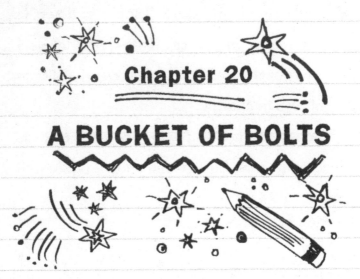

# Chapter 20

## A BUCKET OF BOLTS

My enthusiasm for building a Saturn V is disappearing faster than sweets at a birthday party.

Teamwork is really important.

I was about to give up entirely and go and help Kareem with whatever he was doing when I read about a pretty awesome test of an **F-1 engine**. That's the engine, if you remember, which is found at the bottom of the rocket along with four others. The F-1 engines provide the **7,500,000 pounds of thrust** I'll need to lift off the ground. When it comes to doing the really heavy work, these things pull their weight. Or push it.

The test came about when a group of NASA engineers decided to try fixing up an old F-1 to see if they could get it working again. They faced similar problems to the ones I'm having.

Well, sort of similar. The NASA people had a few advantages over me. They were **engineers**, they worked for NASA, they knew about spaceships and they had access to an old F-1 engine. But hey, let's not worry about the small details for now. Let's just see what they did and what I can do to learn from their experience.

The team began by closely examining every millimetre of the engine. The best way to do

this, as you probably know, is to take it apart.

They laser scanned everything and made new parts for any which needed replacing. But they didn't start the F-1, because testing it would have required equipment to hold it in place and enough space around to prevent the vibrations from shattering windows in homes.

I hadn't even thought about making the parts to hold other parts in place.

I know I don't have access to old parts to scan but at least it's been shown that a small team can make the things they need. The engine is incredibly complicated, so if 3D printing works for that then it should be able to work for the outer shell, the connecting rings, the Command Module, Lunar Module and so on. Right?

I have to keep telling myself this.

I've been reading about how engines work. There are two main parts. One bit delivers the exhaust which provides the thrust needed to lift the rocket. But there's another bit which moves the pumps needed to push fuel which the first part burns.

And then there's the fuel. The rocket equation tells me how much fuel I need, but there are other problems I have to solve.

The Saturn V uses a lot of fuel.

The first stage will require **770,000 litres** of **kerosene** plus **1,204,000 litres** of **liquid oxygen**.

The second stage will require **984,000 litres** of **liquid hydrogen** plus **303,000 litres** of **liquid oxygen**.

The third stage will require **252,750 litres**

of **liquid hydrogen** plus **73,280 litres** of **liquid oxygen**.

The Command Module uses fuel cells instead of liquids, but even so it will require **120 kilograms** of two chemicals. One was called **monomethylhydrazine** and the other was called **nitrogen tetroxide**. These ignited when they came into contact with each other.

The Lunar Module (both for the descent part and the ascent part, though in separate containers) uses a chemical called **'aerozine 50'** which ignites when it comes into contact with **nitrogen tetroxide**. We'll need some of that but, worryingly, I can't find how much I'll need. But I think this is the least of my worries at the moment.

There's a lovely word for the type of fuel used by the Command and Lunar modules: **hypergolic**. It means that it will ignite when

it comes into contact with another chemical.
That's what I need.

I can't, in other words, use my mum's chip
fat oil or drive to my local petrol station and fill
up my spaceship.

This is specialist stuff.

If I'm going to need special permission to
build my rocket and a special place to launch

it, then I just know that there will be a government department in charge of special rocket fuel licenses.

Looking back over the last few pages I can see that I've written about a lot of really tricky things. Understanding HOW a rocket works is one thing and I've done really well on that.

But actually making it is another challenge, and I don't think I'm going to be able to do that.

Perhaps it's time to admit that this project is too big — even for a kid.

## Chapter 21

# STOP THE COUNTDOWN

I'm sitting quietly with all my notes, blueprints and ideas scattered around me. And yes, I'm holding on to my teddy bear because I feel sad.

My big project, which seemed so easy just a few months ago, now seems impossible. I want to write: 'just as I was about to give up entirely, the telephone rang and a mysterious billionaire benefactor promised me all the resources I would need to reach the Moon'.

But I can't.

The theory of building my own Saturn V is solid. I've learnt a lot about how the thousands of NASA people designed and built it all those years ago. I know a lot about what made it so successful and the effort which went into it. I've learnt how Kepler's laws of motion were added to by Isaac Newton, whose theories were really sharpened up by Albert Einstein.

That's a line of thinking which stretches from the **1500s** to the **1900s**, without which we couldn't get into Earth orbit and then on to the Moon.

I even understand how atmospheric pressure affects my body's ability to breathe pure oxygen.

But . . .

I feel as though there might well be a limit to the size of rocket one person can build on her own. I feel as though I've come to a dead end, despite everything I've learnt.

So I'm calling it quits. Which isn't the ending I wanted to write (or that you wanted to read).

But I'm glad I tried. I know more now than I did all those months ago before I began reading and scribbling in my notebook. Perhaps if I can't build my own spaceship and set foot on the Moon, I can inspire someone else — someone like you, even — to work hard and become part of the team who will journey there in the future.

This isn't the end of the story.

Even though I can't quite build my own spaceship (yet), other people are. NASA is working on a project to go back to the Moon and to stay there. There's a thing called the **Artemis Project**, which is hoping to put the first woman (pick me, pick me) on the Moon.

A whole new, super mega-powerful rocket, called the **Space Launch System**, will launch the **Orion spaceship** and enable astronauts to live and work in orbit — just like they do on the International Space Station. Eventually there will be a **Moon base** and regular flights, and then it might even be possible to fly to Mars.

**ESA (the European Space Agency)** are part of this too. They designed a REALLY important part of Orion — the part which supplies electricity, propulsion, air, water and even heat to the spaceship.

China has also said it plans to go to the Moon. The future of Moon exploring is looking fantastic!

But . . . I still want to be a part of making something cool.

So now I'm wondering . . .

## CAN KAREEM BUILD A TIME MACHINE?

After all . . . how difficult can it be?

# GLOSSARY

⭐ **ALDRIN, BUZZ:** Known also as 'Dr Rendezvous', because he was one of the people who figured out how to dock two spaceships together in space. Aldrin was the second person to walk on the Moon as part of the historic Apollo 11 mission in 1969. He's first in this index though!

⭐ **ARMSTRONG, NEIL:** The first man on the Moon! Armstrong was a quiet man who led the historic Apollo 11 mission in 1969. He came up with the dedication: 'One small step for man, one giant leap for mankind'.

⭐ **APOGEE:** If a spaceship is orbiting Earth, its apogee is when it's at its most distant point. The opposite term is 'perigee'.

**APOLLO:** The name given to the missions which used the Saturn V to get to the Moon.

**ARTEMIS PROJECT:** A new mission from NASA which will put people back on the Moon.

**BYTES (KILOBYTES, MEGABYTES, GIGABYTES, TERABYTES):** A way to measure the amount of information storage in a computer.

**CARBON DIOXIDE:** One of the gasses found in Earth's atmosphere and the one we breathe out.

**CELESTIAL NAVIGATION:** The name given to finding our way when travelling using the stars as a sort of map.

**★ COLLINS, MICHAEL:** The pilot of the Command Module for the Apollo 11 mission. Collins stayed in orbit around the Moon when Armstrong and Aldrin walked on the surface.

**★ COMMAND SERVICE MODULE:** The name given to the two parts of the Saturn V which housed the astronauts. The Command Service Module split into the Command Module and the Service Module. Only the Command Module landed back on Earth after the mission was completed.

**★ DRAG:** The force experienced by an object when it moves through an atmosphere.

**★ EARTH:** I've no idea . . . only joking! Earth is the planet where we all live (for now). It's the third closest to the sun.

**EINSTEIN, ALBERT:** A very clever scientist. Einstein figured out how gravity bends space and time.

**ELLIPSE:** A squashed circle.

**ENERGY:** The amount of potential we have in order to move or do anything.

**ESCAPE VELOCITY:** The speed we need to reach in order to get away from the Earth's gravitational pull.

**EUROPEAN SPACE AGENCY:** A team made up of lots of people from all over Europe who work together to do cool space science stuff.

**F-1 ENGINE:** The most powerful engine on the Saturn V.

⭐ **GRAVITY:** The force which pulls everything towards everything else. It keeps us on the ground and if you get caught eating sweets in class then you can say, 'they were caught in the gravitational pull of my mouth'.

⭐ **HELIUM:** A gas which is lighter than air. Used in balloons — the party ones which float on their own — and the ones which fly up into the sky.

⭐ **HYDROGEN:** A gas which, when cooled enough, becomes a liquid which can be used as a fuel for engines.

⭐ **INTERNATIONAL SPACE STATION:** A bunch of rooms stuck together orbiting Earth about 240 miles up. It's constantly lived in by astronauts who carry out experiments which help make life better on Earth (like keeping an eye on our planet), as well as figuring out how to travel and live in space. My number one holiday destination.

★ **INTERSTAGE SKIRT:** A ring-shaped object on the Saturn V which joins one stage of the rocket to another. It's jettisoned when no longer needed.

★ **INVERSE SQUARE LAW:** One of Newton's laws which we can use to work out how much a force (like gravity) will affect us based on how close we are to an object. The further away from Earth we get, the less its gravity will affect us.

★ **ION:** An ion is an electrically charged atom.

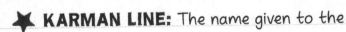

⭐ **KARMAN LINE:** The name given to the imaginary boundary where space officially starts.

⭐ **KEPLER'S FIRST LAW:** This law, discovered and written down by Johannes Kepler, says that a planet will orbit a star (our sun is a star) in an elliptical orbit.

⭐ **KEPLER'S SECOND LAW:** This law says that a line joining an object (like a spaceship) and the thing it's orbiting (like Earth) will cover equal areas in equal amounts of time.

⭐ **KEPLER'S THIRD LAW:** I don't need to worry about this one, but the third law says that the amount of time it takes a planet to orbit the sun is linked to the longest distance it gets on its orbit. Orbits are ellipses, not circles, which means the distance a planet is from the sun will vary as it moves around.

⭐ **LAUNCH:** The act of sending a rocket into the air. Or a boat into the sea. Or of sending something somewhere. Like a sandwich across a room. I didn't mean to though.

⭐ **LUNAR MODULE:** The spaceship which actually landed on the Moon. The descent parts of all six lunar modules which landed on the Moon are still there.

⭐ **MASS:** The amount of stuff which makes up an object. Earth has a lot more mass than a teaspoon. But some objects can be smaller than others and have more mass. For example, a neutron star is so dense that it has a LOT of mass even though they can be smaller than Earth.

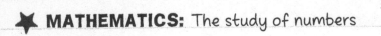

⭐ **MATHEMATICS:** The study of numbers and measuring and order.

⭐ **MICROCLIMATE:** A small, breathable environment — like the one created in a spacesuit.

⭐ **MISSION CONTROL:** The group of people on Earth who help advise and direct astronauts in space.

⭐ **MOON:** A rocky object orbiting a planet.

⭐ **NASA:** An organisation in America which is responsible for missions and science in space.

⭐ **NEUTRON STAR:** The collapsed heart of a star. A neutron star is small and dense, meaning that it exerts a lot of gravitational force for its size.

**NITROGEN:** One of the gasses found in the air we breathe on Earth.

**ORBIT:** The motion of one object around another (like the Moon around the Earth).

**ORBITAL MECHANICS:** The science and maths behind how an object orbits another object.

**PERIGEE:** The closest point an object (like a spaceship or a moon or planet) comes in orbit of something else. The opposite to perigee is 'apogee'.

**PERSONAL LIFE SUPPORT SYSTEM**
The backpack worn by astronauts which contains all the technology needed to keep them alive.

**POO:** The solid (mostly) waste we get rid of after our bodies have finished converting food into energy.

**PRESSURE:** The amount of force put on something. Like the air on our bodies.

**ROCKET:** A device which uses fuels in order to move.

**ROCKET EQUATION:** The calculations needed to work out how much fuel a spaceship or rocket needs in order to get into space.

**SATURN V:** The rocket used for the Apollo missions which put people on the Moon.

**SCRUBBERS:** The system used to extract and hold harmful carbon dioxide from the atmosphere on a spaceship or in a spacesuit.

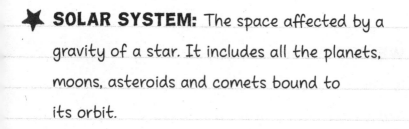 **SOLAR SYSTEM:** The space affected by a gravity of a star. It includes all the planets, moons, asteroids and comets bound to its orbit.

**SPACE:** The name given to the vast area between planets and stars.

**SUN:** The name given to a star — especially our closest star, the one which makes life possible.

**URINE:** The yellow liquid our bodies get rid of as waste. Also known as WEE!

**VON BRAUN, WERNER:** The German rocket scientist who went to America after the

Second World War, and one of the people who helped make the moon landing possible.

⭐ **WEIGHT** The measure of how heavy an object is. This changes depending on the object's mass and the effect of gravity.

# ACKNOWLEDGEMENTS

Writing a book is as much a team effort as any moon landing. Whilst this one did not take 400,000 people, it was only launched thanks to the tireless ingenuity and efforts of a number of people. So with starry-eyed gratitude I'd like to mention the following people:

To my son, Oliver. He's always taking me to new places and pushing me to look back at who I am. To my early readers, Ruth, Fenner, Gary and Ollie, Ralph and Commander Amanda. Brave explorers, every one. And to my science saviours, Alison, Mell and Chris at Thornleigh Salesian College. And, as I wave goodbye before boarding my spaceship, to the wonderful people at UCLan Publishing; Hazel, Jake, Charlotte, Becky and Heidi — your vision put a Dom on the Moon.

# HAVE YOU EVER WONDERED HOW BOOKS ARE MADE?

UCLan Publishing are based in the North of England and involve BA Publishing and MA Publishing students from the University of Central Lancashire at every stage of the publishing process.

BA Publishing and MA Publishing students work closely with our company and work on producing books as part of their course — some of which are selected to be published and printed by UCLan Publishing. Students also gain first-hand experience of negotiating with buyers, conceiving and running innovative high-level events to leverage sales, as well as running content creation business enterprises.

Our approach to business and teaching has been recognised academically and within the publishing industry. We have been awarded Best Newcomer at the Independent Publishing Guild Awards (2019) and a *Times* Higher Education Award for Excellence and Innovation in the Arts (2018).

As our business continues to grow, so too does the experience our students have upon entering UCLan Publishing. To find out more, please visit: www.uclanpublishing.com/courses/